P9-AQP-221

To Mother

Christmas, 1931

"I know of only one person
in the Universe who might
want this book ——
And he's in England."
—— Argument Used in
Reducing the Sale
price of this
Prize Item to a
Reasonable Minimum.

Tales from Bernard Shaw

told in the jungle
by
Gwladys Evan Morris

illustrated
by
Phyllis A. Trery

and published
by
Frederick A. Stokes Company

COPYRIGHT, 1929, BY GWLADYS EVAN MORRIS

Printed in the United States of America

FOREWORD

I AM deeply indebted to Mr. Bernard Shaw, who, with the generosity of the truly great, has allowed me to turn his plays into tales. He calls them "Gwladys' Lambs' Tales from Shaw." I have made no attempt to reproduce his wit, for that would not be possible. All I have attempted, is to reveal, as far as lies in my power, the heart behind it—for Mr. Shaw goes right to the heart. I do not believe there is a shade or grade of feeling that he is not capable of understanding. This is the tribute of a woman to a man.

By zoological and grammatical standards I have committed crimes—intentionally ! I have mated a rhinoceros with a peacock, and their offspring is a bee, a salamander, and a mule ! I have also taken a peacock to represent a female, because in nature—mind you, I'm not saying human nature, I daren't—it is the male that is the emblem of vanity ! I have also used the word 'gooder' because 'better' does not mean what I mean, and 'beautifulness,' because it seems to suit the castle-in-the-air situation in *Arms and the Man*. I should also like to explain that Jack (my chattering monkey) in *Man and Superman* is Shaw himself, as is also the rare old bird in *Fanny's First Play,* and that the woman's part in *Captain Brassbound's Conversion* was written expressly for and round the personality of Ellen Terry.

GWLADYS EVAN MORRIS

CONTENTS

MAJOR BARBARA
or, The Jangle Jungle

MAJOR BARBARA

or, The Jangle Jungle

IN the jangle and jungle of life you must kill or be killed, you must eat or be eaten, you must trap or be trapped.

The great Rhino knew it—had always known it, had prepared for it, had grown a lovely thick skin for it, and long, strong tusks for it. And he hewed his way through the jungle and nothing could stop him and he stopped at nothing—and —ugh !—he was always there, grabbing and getting, spreading and swelling, overtaking, overpowering, overwhelming; nothing could stop him.

But even a Rhino has his soft side, and his soft side made him up one day to look for a mate. Being the Rhino that he was, only the best would satisfy him. Spying a beautiful and haughty Peacock strutting about in her proud way in the dazzling sunshine, he made up his mind.

"I'll have her," said he to himself ; and went after her and won her, and she bore him three offsprings, two she-males and a he, and their names were Barbara, Sarah, and Stephen. Barbara was a Honey-bee, Sarah a Salamander, and Stephen a Mule. (Imagine it !)

Now the Rhinos of old had learned that the he-offspring of a Rhino is never the best Rhino to carry on their business, the business of Death and Destruction ; and so a big boss Rhino before he died would always look out for some other creature upon whom to bestow his Rhino hide, his Rhino tusks, and his Rhino business of destruction. And, as you might have expected, no Mrs Rhino on earth is going to put up with having her he-offspring slighted and passed over for a strange creature ; so it always came to pass that a Mrs Rhino would up and away, taking her family with her, and leaving the Rhino alone with his ruthless business. And this is what had happened at the beginning of my story, so . . .

Once upon a time there was a Mrs Rhino who lived in her home with her three offspring, two she-males and a he, Barbara, Stephen, and Sarah. They, at least the shes, were free and happy and went their own way, but the poor little he had rather allowed himself to be the trapped, the killed, and the eaten. He hated rhinos anyway, and the thought of that dreadful father of his made him shudder—that awful old pachyderm with his Death and Destruction, his grabbing and getting. How wicked he was, and how the Mule hated his wickedness !

Now you must know that Barbara was a teeny-weeny bit of a Rhino herself ; I don't mean, of course, the death and destruction part ; nor the killing and eating part, but the thinking part. She thought the way Rhinos think—big ; her heart was big, and she wanted to do big things, but she didn't want to do them the way the Rhinos do them ; she didn't

He hewed his way through the jungle and nothing
could stop him

want to destroy, she wanted to help, to heal, and to free. How was she to set about it ? That was the question.

Now in the jangle and jungle of life there is an Army of busy, well-ordered little creatures whose mission it is to help, to heal, and to free. And so, as like will always come to like, our Barbara found herself coming to that Army of busy, well-ordered little Bees. And she joined them, and with them found her happiness, for to them came the poor, the broken, the helpless, the bad, the good. And so Barbara got her chance to help, to heal, and to free, and made good use of it. The Army of Bees were proud of her, and made a Major of her, and her honey-words were heard by many, and many were made happy by them. Among the many that heard her honey-words was a slick, knowing, wise young Owl, a strong, powerful creature, an aristocratic creature, and he fell in love with the Honey-bee and pursued her and wooed her and won her, did that persistent, wise young Owl who always got what he wanted in his cool, aristocratic way, without hurting anyone.

Now, the still beautiful and haughty Peacock, the offspring's mother, began to think. She had three offspring, but when they mated (as they were sure to) there would be six. For already Barbara had her wise young Owl and Sarah had her Lizard. And so she wondered whether the gold she had would be enough to go round, because, astute old thing that she was, she felt that as none of her offspring had taken after their father, none of them would be Rhino enough to pick mates with sufficient gold of their own. And as she thought and thought she came to the conclusion that there was only one thing to do— she must send for the Rhino. He would surely come, he surely would like to see his offspring again. Whether his offspring would like to see him, she wasn't so sure ! She sent for the Rhino, the family was aghast. That wicked old Rhino coming to their home !

"How could you do it, Mother ? " " How on earth are we to treat him ? " " What are we to say to him ? " But it was too late to run away—the astute old Peacock had seen to that !

" I want you all to behave beautifully," she said, " and do me credit. Lizard, try not to titter ; Owl, don't dare to be witty ; Salamander, rouse yourself up for once ; and Mule, for heaven's sake, don't be mulish."

And they all promised to do the very best they could, but the Mule was full of disapproval and hatred at the thought of his father's coming.

And the high and haughty Peacock herself, what of her ? Well, she was a She-thing-of-she-things ; you never could tell what *she* would do !

And so the Rhino arrived. It was really a very embarrassing moment. He hadn't seen any of his family for years. He gazed round him with astonishment ; he thought he had only three offspring, and, lo and behold, there were five ! What *is* a poor father to do, you know !

Pulling himself together, he seized on the Lizard and shook

The Army of Bees were proud of her, and made
a Major of her

him heartily by the hand, greeting him as his first-born. The Lizard tittered and tittered.

The Peacock was dumbfounded.

" Do you mean to say, Rhino, that you don't know your own offspring ? "

" Well, my dear, does any father ? "

" Silence ! Your wickedness shall not contaminate my family. This is Stephen."

The Mule instantly became mulish. The Rhino did what he could to be pleasant, but as soon as he decently could he went over to the wise young Owl, and shook him warmly.

" You must be my son," said he.

" I am afraid you flatter me," twitted the Owl ; " I am only the Owl in love with Barbara ; let me explain everyone to you " ; which was the only wise thing to be done. It was really very difficult and embarrassing. The Lizard began to titter again ; the Salamander began to take an interest ; the Owl began to be witty ; the Rhino began to be ruthless ; the Mule went on being mulish. But the Bee was there with her honey-words, and soothed them all and smoothed the difficulties over.

The Rhino looked at her. " You must be Barbara," he said, " and I can see by your dress that you belong to the Army of Bees. ' Blood and Fire ' is their motto, isn't it ?—the same as mine."

" But it's not the same sort of blood and fire, don't you know," tittered the Lizard, " their fire purifies."

" Yes, indeed," said the Mule, mulishly. " Right's right, and wrong's wrong, and you can't tell me there is anything right in your Death and Destruction business."

" Perhaps," said the Honey-bee, softly, " we might find something if we went to look."

The great Rhino thrilled at her words. There spoke his own daughter.

Now, because of the teeny-weeny bit of Rhino in the Bee, and because like will always come to like, the Bee and the Rhino —the father and the daughter, began to come together. They seemed to understand each other. That Honey-bee would win her father from his Destruction business. She wanted him to see her with her Army, helping, healing, freeing ; she asked him to come. He told her he would make a compact with her ; if he came to see her business, she must come to see his. She consented, warning him that he might be tempted to join her Army. He consented, warning her that she might be tempted to join his. And so, in this jangle and jungle of life, Fate plays her tricks.

The Rhino went next day to see Barbara's Army and watch her operations. There he saw his daughter, his wonderful daughter, spending herself on the poor, the broken, the disillusioned, and the starved. There he saw the result of the difference between the Rhino philosophy of the strong, the ruthless, the grabbing, the getting, the succeeding, and the philosophy of the selfless, the honest, the kind, the weak, the thriftless, and the content. He wanted his daughter away from it all ; he would get her away, too. He would bide his time, but he would find a way ; he, the Rhino, would find a way to gain the love and respect of his daughter with the teeny-weeny bit of the Rhino in her.

Now the difficulties of running the Army of the Bees were very great, because the business consisted of giving, and giving isn't business ; and so the Army had to resort to all sorts of unbusinesslike methods to keep itself going. It had to beg. Now begging took time, and Barbara was finding that out, and it disconcerted her to realise that it took up the time that she wanted to devote to the healing, the helping, and the freeing.

The Rhino, watching, saw it too, and saw his chance approaching. Fate, the jade, was playing into his hands !

"What do you think, Major Barbara," said another Major Bee, flying in, full of excitement, "the great Hippo Sax has promised to give us five thousand tons of honey if five other Rhinos or Hippos will give a thousand each !"

The whole army became uproarious at the wonderful news.

"Who is Hippo Sax ? " said Barbara. "I've never heard of him."

"He's Bodger—Bodger's Beverages, my dear," said the Rhino.

"Bodger's Beverages ! " said Barbara, aghast. "Why, he brings more Death and Destruction than even you do, Father ! "

"Well," said the Rhino, "I would like to give the other five thousand tons, if it's only for the pleasure of making old Bodger pay up ! "

" Oh," said the other Major, almost weeping with joy, " I knew my prayers would be answered. Oh, God be with you ! "

" Stop ! " It was the tragic voice of Barbara.

" Major ! " they all cried, " What is wrong ? "

" Do you think I ought not to take the honey ? " asked the other Major, wistfully.

" No, no ! You must take it, dear," said Barbara bravely ; " you are doing it for the best ; the Army must be kept going at all costs. But to think that it must take that tainted honey, wrought out of Death and Destruction, drink and ruin ! I can't bear it ! I just can't bear it ! "

The heart of the noble Honey-bee was broken, and she sank to the ground in despair.

" March on ! March on ! " she cried heroically. And so the Army, headed by the other Major, the Rhino, and the Owl, marched onward.

Our Honey-bee, feeling forsaken, useless, and alone, went home to take off the uniform of the Bees whose mission is to help, to heal, and to free. But God, or Fate, had by no means forsaken Barbara. Fate knew what she was about all right. The first round was over, that was all. Barbara was being prepared for the second.

The family returned to find her no longer dressed in the uniform of the Bees, and were surprised beyond words ; the

Owl's heart went out to his beloved, and the Lizard did his best to comfort her ; but Barbara was not to be comforted. And then in came the Rhino.

"Barbara, my daughter, is it true that I have caused you unhappiness ? "

'Do you think I can be happy in this tawdry dress, Father, after having worn the uniform of the Bees ? Listen. Yesterday a young fighting Cock came to our headquarters in search of his mate. He had come to peck her eyes out for daring to leave him. But I got at him. I made him feel, I made him think, I even got him to the pitch of wanting to give a Bee twenty pieces of corn to compensate her for his having pecked at her for being the cause of his mate leaving him. Twenty pieces of corn was nearly all he had in the world, so that was pretty good for a start. But I told him he couldn't *buy* his salvation and ease his conscience that way. I told him he must give up being a fighting Cock, for we wouldn't be satisfied with anything less, and we refused to take his corn. And then you came along with your five thousand tons of honey, and we were forced to take it ; forced to allow *you* to buy *your* salvation, simply because the Army couldn't afford to refuse your offer. You can imagine the effect of that on my fighting Cock. He left us disgusted, disillusioned, lost, knowing that the only difference between him and you was that he couldn't offer to pay us enough. I have lost my fighting Cock, Father, that I had almost turned into a dove, and have been the means of turning him into a wolf. I can never forgive you for that, and I can never wear the Bees' uniform again. You and Bodger have bought me out with your tainted honey gold ! "

The great Rhino looked at his daughter, and understood.

" Does a daughter of mine despair so easily ? " he said gravely. " Can she really believe that she can strike a living creature to the heart, and leave no mark upon him ? "

" Father, you are a magician, or a devil ! I don't know which you are, but you are right. He cannot be lost for ever. What was I thinking of ? Where was my faith ? You have given it back to me, may God bless you for that ! And now take me to see your Destruction business, for you have given me the strength to bear it."

So the family started away prepared to face the misery, the horror, and the evil of the Death and Destruction business. But, lo ! there was no misery or horror to be seen, no cruelty or dreadfulness, all was absurdly, horribly, ridiculously perfect. Beautiful cottages, beautiful gardens, flowers, birds, and butter-flies. Even where they made the Death and Destruction weapons there were armies of sturdy, happy looking he-things, making enough gold to mate and keep their mates and offspring contented and happy. What did it mean ? Was there no evil, then ? No right and wrong ? The family were speechless. Stephen was the most astounded and the most abashed ; he felt he had made a fool of himself by underrating and misjudging his father so completely. Even the Lizard found nothing to titter at ; Sarah woke up completely, and Barbara was spellbound. And the wise young Owl, what of him ? He was thinking, thinking very hard.

"Good gracious, Rhino ! " said the Peacock, the She-thing-of-she-things, "fancy your having kept this to yourself all these years. And why have you pretended that it was all Death and Destruction, misery and horror ? "

The Rhino was tickled at that.

"And what is all this nonsense you've talked about finding another creature upon whom to bestow the Rhino business ? " continued the Peacock. "If I hear another word about it, I shall have you locked up. Mind you, I am no longer asking for it for Stephen, he is far too mulish ; almost as mulish as you are yourself," said she, racing on so that no one should have a chance of getting a word in. "But what about Barbara ? She is your offspring, and she has a right to it. And, if you must have a strange creature, though I don't hold with any of that Rhino rubbish, why not let the strange creature be our wise young Owl, so that when he mates with Barbara, the Rhino business will still belong to the Rhinos ? "

Plumb, right into the bull's-eye ! The She-thing-of-she-things had hit the nail on the head. It was just what the Rhino wanted ; it was just what the wise young Owl wanted too. But what of Barbara, was it what she wanted ?

"My love," said the Rhino in his most courtly manner (he was a gallant old thing, you know), "you are a brilliant and beautiful creature. You are my mate ; together we have created the soul of a Rhino in one of our offspring. This has never happened before in the whole history of the Rhinos. But will our Barbara consent to it ? However bright and happy, clean and good the Rhino business *looks,* will she not always see in it nothing but Death and Destruction ? For she will never, nor will the wise young Owl ever become a Rhino. She will never grow long, strong tusks, nor a strong, thick skin. How shall we find a way out ? To run a big business you must be a big creature, you must be a Rhino, or a Hippo . . ."

" Or an Elephant ! " suggested the Peacock.

" Ah ! " said the Rhino, " the Elephant ! I'd forgotten her. I wonder . . .

" And now to business "—the Rhino never wasted time. He called the Owl.

" And what does the great Rhino want of me ? " twinkled the Owl (who knew perfectly well what was coming !).

" Owl," said the Rhino, " I am going to offer you the Rhino business. You are exactly the kind of strange, new creature that we want to keep our business alive. What do you say ? "

" I say that you are a wicked old devil, Rhino, trying to buy my soul ! "

" Well, never mind that for the moment," said the Rhino. " Let us merely go into the price of your soul. I propose to offer you a thousand pieces of gold per year for it."

"*Ugh !*" said the wise young Owl, scornfully, "I want five times that amount. I can do without your Rhino business," said he craftily, "but you can't do without me. Besides, I shall be your son-in-law when I mate with Barbara."

"Leave my soul out of this, Owl, it's yours that's up for sale, not mine," said Barbara.

"True, true," said the Owl, unabashed. "Well, Rhino, five thousand gold pieces is my price."

"I'll offer you half," said the Rhino, imperturbably.

"Half !" echoed the Owl, disgustedly.

"Half," said the Rhino, firmly.

"All right," said the Owl, cheerfully, "I'll take half. I would have taken a fifth ! I don't think much of your business capabilities, paying an owl, a perfect owl, who knows nothing whatever about your business, five times as much as he would have taken."

"Don't you," answered the Rhino, with a smile. "Well, this is the way I look at it. If you can get five times the value of anything out of me, you can get it out of anyone, and that will be good for the business."

The family were amazed, they were beginning to realise the greatness of the Rhino.

"Well, now that we have decided on your price—what about the business itself ? Are you accepting it or not ?"

"How am I going to reconcile it to my soul ?"

" Oh ! that's easy," said the Peacock, cheerfully, " sell your weapons of destruction only to the good people."

" None of that ! " said the Rhino, shortly ; " you must sell them to anyone who can pay for them."

" Look here, Rhino ! If I decide to take the business on, I shall have the power, not you."

" From the moment you enter the business, your power will not be your own," said the Rhino, gravely.

" To whom will it belong, then ? " asked Barbara.

" To a Power of which we all are part."

" Father, is that true ? " said Barbara, earnestly. " Or are you trying to lay a snare for me ? "

" It is true," said the Rhino.

" But does the Power *wish* for death and destruction ? "

" It wishes its creatures to have power, for it knows they cannot save their souls without it. I saved your soul, Barbara, through my power."

" You saved my soul ! " cried Barbara, in a voice of horror. " What do you mean ? "

" When you were with the Bees' Army, didn't you notice that you had to spend most of your time getting the necessary honey gold to keep the thing going, and that this left you less time for the saving of souls ? Well, I saved your soul by providing gold enough to allow you time enough to grow a soul. That is why to be poor is the greatest crime on earth, because it takes up our time and keeps us chained to earth, leaving us no time for the heaven. Take the Rhino business on, Owl, and you will be providing Barbara with time enough and power enough to fulfil her destiny. Without them she can do nothing."

The Owl was genuinely astonished. Could it be possible that the old Rhino was a great soul, after all ?

" My mind is made up," said the Owl in ecstasy ; " I will take on the business. And now, beloved," said the brave creature, turning to his mate, " have I lost you for ever ? "

" Of course not, you Owl you," said Barbara, with tears in her eyes, taking him in her arms. " You'd have lost me if you had refused. I understand at last. Father was right after all."

And so Barbara became a Rhino, and took on her father's business with her beloved wise young Owl. But because of the long, strong tusks, and the strong, thick skins of the Rhinos of old, all the grabbing and getting, the trapping and spreading, the killing and eating, the overpowering and overwhelming was done, and the power was won. The old Rhino was right : he had saved her soul from that. So she had no need of those long, strong tusks, nor had she any need of the small, strong horn : and because she had no need of it it softened but it grew, so that in time it became like an arm helping, healing, freeing the hearts of the creatures working in that Death and Destruction business. And she listened to those hearts, and because she listened her ears softened and they grew, so that she heard and understood and was able to wield a greater power than ever before.

So that in time the great Rhino became less like a Rhino, and more like the great creature we call the Elephant ; indeed, that is how the Elephant came into being, and became the friend of man. For the Elephant is the aristocrat of beasts, and when *we* become as big and strong we shall all become as kind and wise, and the jangle and jungle of life will be a jangle and jungle no longer.

CANDIDA

or, The Awakening of the King

CANDIDA

or, The Awakening of the King

ONCE upon a time there was a beautiful, serene queen called Candida. She did not live in a palace, like other queens, but in a tiny castle, overlooking a little park that was named after another queen—Victoria—in London Town.

She had a son and a daughter and a husband whom she had for a king. You will, of course, think this is a funny way to talk about a king, but to tell you the truth, he wasn't really a king at all *in the inside of him*, but the Queen had made him *look like one* on the outside. You must know, first of all, that he was a particular kind of king. He was a king of souls. He had a beautiful voice, and a beautiful manner ; he went about his kingdom teaching his people to be good and healthy and happy, and everybody believed in him and came to listen to him because he was always good and healthy and happy himself.

How did he manage to be good and healthy and happy all the time ? As it isn't very easy, I will tell you. He didn't manage it himself at all ; it was the Queen who managed it for him.

Whenever any beggars came knocking at the castle gate, and there was money in the house to spare, the Queen would call the King and send him out to them, and the King would give them money and kind words, and they would go away blessing him and telling all the people ; but when there was no money to spare, she would go herself so that they would go away not blessing her, and so in this way, and in every other way, she built a castle of comfort and indulgence and love all round him and made him King and master. And they lived happily, and the King was pleased with himself and his wife and his home and his work—until it happened, one day, that he met a lonely knight, who was a poet, gazing into the river. The King's kind heart went out to him, and he took him home with him.

And the moment the Knight saw the Queen he loved her. He did not tell her so, but the more he saw of her beautiful queenly ways, the more his love grew and grew. Now, by queenly ways, I do not mean the old-fashioned kind of queenly ways—lying about on beautiful couches and having beautiful slaves to wait on one. No, I mean queenly ways like the queen's in chess, who darts about, seeing to everything herself, keeping her eye always on the alert for anything that might check the good and happy life of the king.

Now a knight can be a very dangerous person to have about because he can jump right through people's disguises and right into their very thoughts ; and one dreadful day he did both together and discovered the King, just as he was, with no disguise on whatsoever ! He was so appalled at finding out that

And the moment the Knight saw the Queen he loved her

the King was not a king at all, and not even as knightly as he was himself, that in that moment he made up his mind to speak out.

"I love the Queen," he burst forth.

"Of course you do, everybody does," replied the King in his most kingly and gracious manner.

"It's no use your trying to be kingly with me because I can see through you, and you aren't a king at all. I know the people think you are. I've seen you with them, but you can't deceive me—or the Queen."

"What!" shouted the King, beside himself with rage at the mention of his beloved Queen, and he seized the Knight roughly by the tunic.

"Don't touch me. I shall kill myself if you do!" shrieked the Knight, which wasn't knightly at all, but he couldn't bear to be touched by anyone he despised.

"You horrible, cowardly little puppy, leave my castle at once," commanded the King, delighted at having frightened the Knight and being able to feel superior and kingly once more. But it was short-lived because, as I told you before, the Knight could jump from point to point with wonderful quickness and cleverness.

"I am not afraid of you. You are afraid of me," was the amazingly reply.

"Yes, it looks like it," said the King, contemptuously.

"Yes, it does," said the Knight. "You *are* afraid of me;

Tales from Bernard Shaw

you are afraid of my ideas. You call yourself the King of Souls! Well, to be that, you have to have at least three qualities that belong to a soul. First, you have to know yourself as you really are ; second, you have to have courage ; and, third, you have to have truth. And you haven't any of these things."

"I have them all," said the King, majestically.

"No, you haven't," contradicted the Knight. "I will prove it to you. First of all, you didn't know you weren't a king until I told you. Secondly, you order me out of your house, which shows you are afraid of me. And now, before I go any further, I must put a question to you. Shall you tell the Queen about our quarrel ? "

"No, a thousand times, no ! " shouted the King.

"Ah! The third a lie! A lie! " cried the Knight in triumph. "I told you there was no truth in you. Good-bye, Mr King of Souls."

At that dreadful moment the Queen appeared in the door-way and was amazed at seeing the Knight with his tunic all awry. She went toward him hastily and tidied him up ; and when she had done that, she thought he looked so nice and handsome that she told him he had better stay and eat with them.

"Oh, Queen, I am the happiest of men ! " And out they went together.

"And so was I an hour ago," groaned the poor King, as he sank down and buried his head in his hands. And all the things the Knight had said danced around in his heart and trampled it down, making it very heavy ; so much so, that he knew he could not go out that day to help his people to be good and healthy and happy. And there he stayed, all alone, until it was time to eat.

When the Queen returned, her alert eye saw at once that something was troubling her King. So she made him come and talk to her, and they talked about many things. And then she talked about the Knight, and every word she said was like an arrow piercing his heart, because she said things that were like the things the Knight had said, and when he heard them from the Queen's own lips his heart misgave him utterly, and he began to feel alone for the first time in all his life. And he felt his castle tumbling about his ears and he came utterly to the bottom of himself.

And then, of course, he forced himself to look about him for the first time in his life. And he saw one thing to do, and he resolved to do it, and it was the first brave and kingly thing he had ever done. He resolved to go and talk to his people after all, so as to leave the Knight alone with his Queen ; for then he knew he would know once for all whether the Queen wanted him or the Knight most.

And the Knight looked on and marvelled at the brave deed of the King.

When the King had gone, the Queen and the Knight sat together before the fire.

Now it is part of a Knight's code never to betray a trust. He knew that the King had done a brave deed in trusting him alone with his Queen, so he made up his mind to read his poems to her, and not stop, or talk to her ; because, although he was trying hard to be good, he knew that he was not really good. So that when the Queen took up the poker, he became ashamed and uneasy, because he thought she had taken it up to defend herself against him because he had failed to put his drawn sword between them, which, as a true knight, he should have done under those circumstances.

But the Queen did not think a drawn sword necessary ; she knew the Knight to be gooder and stronger than he knew himself to be, and she wanted him to find it out for himself. So she put him to the test and invited him to come and sit at her feet. But he, because of his guilty inside, refused ; but she invited him again, and so he came to sit at her feet because he was weak, and, because he was weak, he was bad at that moment.

But the Queen, knowing quite well the knightly qualities of her Knight, guided him back to his code. And then the Knight began to realise, through her goodness, that he was in Heaven, and he felt the flaming sword inside of him melting away all that was bad. For the other name of the flaming sword is ' love,' and love melts away all the hard and bad things inside ourselves and other people. And so he dared to be himself and call her Candida with all his heart and soul.

Then Candida, seeing that he had won his battle and was all good, put him to the test once again, and asked him if he wanted *anything at all from her*. And he answered : " No, I have come into Heaven, where want is unknown." And the Queen was happy because she saw that the Knight was in Heaven, which means, in other words, that he was good.

And at that moment, in came the King.

Now the King, although he was a King of Souls, had never been in Heaven, so that when he saw his Queen and the Knight in Heaven, he did not understand, and straightway fell into hell, and all the demons of jealousy and suspicion and anger danced about inside him. When the Queen went out to look after things in her usual queenly way the King roughly commanded the Knight to explain.

But the more the Knight tried to explain, the less the King understood. And in the end the King decided that the Queen must choose between them. And no sooner had he decided that than the Queen came back.

When he told her what he had decided she was angry, because, although she was a beautiful, wise, good Queen, she was something more—she was a woman, and she knew that she belonged to herself. So she laughed at them and asked each of them what they had to offer. She asked the King first, and the poor King, who did not understand himself or his Queen, said, in his ignorance, that he offered her his strength, and his honesty, and his power, and his industry. Then she turned to the Knight, and asked him what he had to offer. But the Knight, because of his gift of seeing through people's disguises, knew of the beautiful, tender, loving, but also strong, industrious nature of the Queen herself, so that he offered her his weakness, his need of her, and his utter loneliness without her. The Queen was so amazed at the insight of the Knight that she praised him for his offer. The King, in his agony of fear at having lost her (as he thought), cried out, but the Knight upbraided him for taking an unfair advantage. The Queen, however, had greater insight than even the Knight, and, after having looked at them both very hard, she said :

" I give myself to the weaker of the two."

You must be very surprised that a queen should choose the weaker, because all the queens of old used always to choose the strongest and bravest. Well, to tell you the truth, years ago she thought she had chosen the strongest and the bravest, but she soon found out that however brave and strong they are, they are just the same as if they are weak.

Which was the weaker of the two ? The King was weaker, though he did not know it, and that is why he was weaker, because he did not know it. So that when she said what she did, he broke down utterly, thinking he had lost. But the Knight knew, and the Knight's heart went white at the hurt of losing his love.

But he had been in Heaven, and so bore his hurt nobly. And, because he did so, something wonderful happened to him,

He broke down utterly, thinking he had lost. But the Knight knew

inside, and he knew in that moment that he had power—power to create something which was greater than his own happiness.

And out he fled, eager to start his work.

But the Queen's work was there, in the castle, by the side of her King.

MAN AND SUPERMAN

or, The Trapping of the He-thing

MAN AND SUPERMAN

or, The Trapping of the He-thing

ONCE upon a time, very, very high up in the heavens, there lived two sprites, a He-sprite and a She-sprite, and each of them lived in a ring, and the rings lay one inside the other. The larger ring was called the Ring of Immortal Life, and gave the power of creating new creatures. The smaller ring was called the Ring of Immortal Light and gave the power of creating new things. The She-sprite lived inside the larger, and the He-sprite lived inside the smaller. And there they were ; they couldn't get out because they always went round and round in a ring, you see.

But one day the She-sprite happened to look out of her ring and she saw the He-sprite for the first time ; in that moment she loved him. Now love is the most powerful thing in all the world, and so, because she loved him, she immediately wanted to use that power with which the Ring of Immortal Life endowed her—the power to create new creatures.

She had heard, of course, that the earth was made for that, and so she planned a way to get the He-sprite out of his ring and take him with her to earth. And she did, and away they flew and flew, until at last they reached the earth. There, to her surprise, they were met by quite a severe person with a book of rules under her arm. She was called Dame Nature, and she told them that they must hurry up and find homes—and separate ones, too, as they weren't allowed to fly about the earth in that fashion. Then she took them to a huge forest and parted them.

"Oh, dear! Oh, dear!" said the poor little She-sprite, when she found herself alone. "This is worse than before. What was the use of escaping from our rings to be parted like this? How shall I ever find a home in this huge forest?"

Just then her eyes fell upon something which reminded her of home.

Now when we are away we are always attracted by anything that reminds us of home, and the thing that had reminded this little sprite of her home was something that looked like a ring. She crept closer to it. It *was* a ring! She knew, of course, that it wasn't the Ring of Immortal Life, because it was solid, like everything else she had seen upon the earth.

"Whatever can it be?" she thought to herself. Then an idea came to her. "It's a Ring of Mortal Life," and a thrill of joy ran through her, because she knew that she had found her home at last. She crept still closer to it; she touched it gently; it woke up, it looked at her; it smiled; it seemed to recognise her; then it opened its heart right out to her and took her in, and they became one.

And the Sprite was happy because she knew that through this Ring of Mortal Life she would some day win her He-sprite.

Now the name we give on earth to this Ring of Mortal Life that lives in a forest is 'snake,' and that is what she had become, a beautiful baby snake.

As she lay curled up under the trees in the sunshine some other animals gathered round her. There was a gentle, loving Ring-dove, a clever, chattering He-monkey, a dear old-fashioned He-ass, and a pathetically rebellious, but utterly helpless, She-white-rabbit.

Now, though they were only animals, living in a forest, all of them had names, and the name of the beautiful baby snake was Ann.

"Strange," said the She-sprite, within her heart. "That was my name before I came to earth!"

The gentle, loving Ring-dove was Ricky Ticky Tavy; the clever, chattering He-monkey was Jack; the dear old-fashioned He-ass was Roebuck, and the pathetically rebellious, but utterly helpless She-white-rabbit was, strangely enough, the baby snake's mother. And then there was her father, too.

Now the snake loved that Monkey, Jack, had always loved him, and he had always told her about his adventures in the tree-tops where she could never go, and all the things he ever did, whether they were good or whether they were bad, and that is how she had come to know so much about the He-thing, because he had always talked, you see, but she had always listened.

It fell out, however, that one day something happened to

that Monkey, Jack, something he did not wish to tell her, and this is what it was.

But, first of all, you must remember that we left the He-sprite from the Ring of Immortal Light at the entrance of the forest, looking for his home. *He* wasn't a bit afraid of being left alone, not he. He didn't care a bit about the severe Dame Nature person. He was going to take his time looking for his home ; he found the forest so interesting.

" What a wonderful place," thought he to himself. " But I could make it far more wonderful." And he began to think of all the things he could do, *if only he had the chance.* " That's it," he said, " my home is my chance, so I shall have to find one, after all, I suppose."

You see we always have to obey Dame Nature's rule in the end.

Just at that moment the clever, chattering He-monkey came swinging along from tree to tree in the cleverest manner imaginable.

" Hi," said the He-sprite. " Hi, I like you ! What's your name ? "

" Jack," said the Monkey. " What's yours ? "

" Jack," said the Sprite.

" Are you clever, too ? " said the Monkey.

" Yes," said the Sprite.

" Well," said the Monkey, " I have a mind to take you in." And he did so and they became one.

There was a gentle, loving Ring-dove, a clever, chattering He-monkey, a dear old-fashioned He-ass, and a pathetically rebellious, but utterly helpless, She-white-rabbit

The Sprite was happy because he had found his home, and he knew he could now, through the Monkey, improve that forest and make it fit to live in. And this is the thing he did not want to tell that serpent Ann ; because he now wanted to go off by himself and do his work, and he felt she might try to prevent him.

" I wonder what's happened to that Monkey, Jack," thought Ann to herself. " He's much better behaved than he used to be, but he doesn't seem to belong so much to me ! He is always chopping down this and that and tearing things up and making the other animals fearfully cross and uncomfortable. They don't understand what he's doing a bit, nor do I, really, but I do admire him and I do want him for my very own."

Jack didn't know a bit that she wanted *him* for her very own ; he always thought she wanted Ricky Ticky Tavy. If he had known, it would have terrified him ; he was afraid of that beautiful Snake, he always had been. But the more he escaped her, the more powerful and subtle she became, because of the Sprite of Immortal Life within her heart.

" What can I do to trap him and bind him to me for ever ? " whispered Ann to her Sprite.

" Make him your keeper," it answered.

" I will," said Ann, and she went in search of her father. " Father," she said, " don't you think it would be a very good thing to make that clever, chattering Monkey my keeper ? He is so wise."

"Well, my dear," said her father, "what about my friend, the dear old-fashioned He-ass? He will expect to be your keeper, and he is so respectable."

"Make them both my keepers," said Ann, and she smiled, because she knew how cross they would both of them be!

Of course it was absurd, really, for anyone to be her keeper, because everyone knew how much cleverer a serpent is than any of the other animals—except, perhaps, the clever, chattering Monkey; and this is where the whole story lies.

The Monkey was furious when he found out that he had to be keeper to a powerful, subtle She-thing when he wanted to be off in the forest. And the old-fashioned He-ass was furious at being tied to the clever, chattering Monkey. Not that he thought him clever, he didn't a bit! He only thought him mischievous and shameless; and in his rage he forgot his dignity and told him so.

The Monkey was delighted, because it gave him the chance of calling the old-fashioned He-ass an old-fashioned He-ass to his face, which he did.

"What?" brayed the He-ass, "I am not old-fashioned. I am clever."

"You can't be clever," grinned the Monkey; "if you were you would know better than to call me mischievous and shameless. All the asses do that! It is only *clever* animals who can see that I am clever."

"You are shameless," he repeated, furiously. "Look at you

—always getting up on your hind legs when every self-respecting animal goes about on all fours."

" Yes, with their noses on the ground," grinned the Monkey.

" Well, that's better than chopping things down in the forest and showing up things that we ought not to know about, much less *see* ! " screamed the He-ass. " You're not fit to be Ann's keeper. I shall refuse to act with you."

" It's no use," sighed the Monkey. " I've been refusing all the morning, but you can't argue with her, she's got no legs, she just glides in and out and round about you till you don't know where you've got to."

Just as the poor He-ass was trying to think of something brilliant to say, the gentle, loving Ring-dove came in with the pathetically rebellious, but utterly helpless, She-white-rabbit— Ann's mother—and Ann.

" Ann," said the He-ass, trying to regain his dignity, " I'm afraid I must ask you to choose one of us for your keeper, we can't possibly work together." And he looked disgustedly at the Monkey.

" Mamma," began Ann in her soft and cooing voice.

" Now don't drag me in," squeaked the She-white-rabbit.

" Mamma," continued Ann, taking no notice of her poor mother's interruption, " knows how utterly helpless she is, and poor dear father knew it, too ; that is why he appointed me two keepers. So I *must* abide by his wishes, mustn't I ? " And she glided away, smiling her snaky smile ; because she knew she had the Monkey safely in her trap.

"I knew she'd say that," screamed the Monkey. But he didn't know that she had laid the trap, clever as he was. "Bother her ! I don't want to be her keeper. It will take up a silly lot of time, and she will do just as she likes and blame it all on us if it goes wrong. Ricky Ticky Tavy, you will have to marry her, after all."

Now Ricky Ticky Tavy loved that she-thing, Ann, with all his gentle, loving heart—had always loved her—and he couldn't bear to hear that Monkey, Jack, say such awful things about her. He couldn't see that she was a subtle, snaky thing. He thought she was a dove with angel's wings.

"Yes, Tavy," continued Jack, "you will have to marry her, and I had set my heart on saving you from her."

"What ? Save me from everlasting happiness, Jack ? " he cried.

"Everlasting happiness ! " snapped the Monkey. "There's no such thing. Ann's a serpent ! That's what she is, and once she gets hold of you she will never let you go."

"Oh, Jack," said the Ring-dove, not knowing whether to be delighted at the thought of being her victim or angry at Jack for calling his dove with angel's wings a serpent. But he hurried off to find her, nevertheless. Now everybody thought that Ann was going to marry Tavy ; everybody thought so, even the clever, chattering Monkey.

You can't argue with her . . . she just glides . . . round about you till
you don't know where you've got to

Jack was funny about that she-thing, Ann. She fascinated him, in spite of himself ; she eluded him. He knew, of course, that he was much cleverer than she was, and yet she always seemed to get the better of him. She was subtle, you see, but he was only clever !

" Jack," she whispered, " are you angry at having to be my keeper ? "

" Your keeper ? " he snapped scornfully. " You know quite well you don't need any keeper."

" Oh, Jack," cooed the Snake, trying to get him into a good humour, " let us talk of the times when we used to play together in the sunshine, under the trees—those happy times when you used to tell me everything, till suddenly one day you stopped and became all grown-up. What happened to you ? " whispered Ann.

" Something came to me," said the Monkey.

" What ? " said Ann.

" A sprite," said Jack.

" A sprite ? " repeated Ann. (" Oh, but he's not so powerful as my Sprite—I know him," whispered Ann to the little Ann within her heart.) " Oh, tell me about him," she said.

" Well, one day the Sprite from the Ring of Immortal Light came flashing into my mind, making it all clear, so that I could see everything that was wrong with the forest, and how full it was of old-fashioned weeds, and how I was the person to destroy them and make the place fit to live in."

" Dear me ! " said Ann, rather bored that he wasn't talking about her, " I am afraid I am too feminine to see any sense in destroying. I can create, which is far more wonderful."

" Don't be so silly and ignorant," said the Monkey. " You have to destroy so as to make room to create. I mean to do both, and I don't want to be tied to anyone, and I won't be."

" Nobody wants you to be, Jack," she whispered. " I don't mind your having all those funny ideas about clearing the forest a bit."

" Of course *you* don't, because you can glide in and out of anything, you *serpent*, you ! "

Fancy calling a serpent one to her face ! Most of them would have been furious. But not Ann ! She saw what a wonderful opportunity the clever Monkey had unwittingly given her. She smiled her smile.

When Jack saw that smile he was amazed. " What, you scandalous creature, you ! " said he. " Aren't you going to pretend you're not a serpent ? "

" I never pretend with you, Jack," she cooed. " You see, I know why you called me a serpent. It's because I can do this." And with that she coiled herself right round that amazed and somewhat terrified Monkey's neck !

" What magnificent audacity ! " said the Monkey (he thought he was safe). " It's all right for me, I'm not your victim, you are only playing with me ; but poor Ricky Ticky Tavy ! Poor Ring-dove ! "

" Poor goose ! " said Ann to herself, looking at that clever Monkey and wondering why he was so stupid. And then the others came back, and she had to uncoil herself from round his neck and let him go.

Now Jack was quite an important and powerful Monkey, and as he was fond of flying he had searched the forest until he had found a special and unique Hawk—whose name was 'Enry. Now 'Enry flew very well and fast—almost too fast for his master, who, to tell the truth, was always afraid of falling and breaking his neck ; and one day Jack asked his Hawk not to go so fast.

" What," said the Hawk, disgustedly, " not go so fast ? Look here, Mister Jack, if you wants to go for a ride on a hedge-hog, you go ; but if you wants an 'awk, you got to put up with 'im as 'e is."

Now you may wonder that the Monkey allowed the Hawk to treat him like that, but, as I told you before, he was a unique kind of hawk. He had a funny mind, and amused Jack, and understood him. He also understood something that Jack didn't understand, and one day he was going to tell him. Now just at that moment the far-seeing eye of the Hawk caught sight of Ann, coming toward them, so he just gave a peculiar little whistle and took himself off.

Jack certainly noticed that whistle, but was too busy in his ' clearing the forest' mood to take much notice—so much so that when Ann came up, before he had time to think what he was doing, he asked her why on earth she didn't get rid of all her subtle, snaky ways once and for all.

"You are so unreasonable, Jack," she replied. "I've got to have some weapon to protect myself against the animals in the forest. What else can I do?"

"You can come for a long flight with me on my Hawk, and blow them away for ever," he answered.

"Thank you," said the snaky Ann, seizing the amazing chance the poor foolish Monkey had unwittingly given her. "Thank you. You are my keeper, so I am sure there could be no harm in it. I will come."

"What!" screamed the Monkey, realising in a flash what a fool he had been. But he couldn't think of anything cleverer to say than that the utterly helpless She-white-rabbit, her mother, wouldn't allow it.

"Oh, I don't mind," said the She-white-rabbit, coming up at that moment.

"Come then and make my travelling skin ready," said the serpent, Ann, as she hurried her mother away before another word could be said.

When she was well out of sight the Hawk flew back.

"'Enry," said Jack, "I've just been crazy enough to arrange for Miss Ann and Mr Ricky Ticky Tavy to come flying with us. Now I shall sit by you, and leave the other two together, on your tail."

"That's all right, sir, but what about the lidy's views?" ('Enry meant the serpent by 'the lidy.')

"Oh, she will be as pleased to be with her Ring-dove as he will be to be with her," said the Monkey innocently.

The Hawk stared at him blankly. "Oh, will she? Oh!" And again he gave his peculiar little whistle.

"Look here, 'Enry, why on earth do you make that peculiar little whistle every time Miss Ann's name is mentioned? What do you mean by it?"

"Mean to say you dunno, guv'nor?"

"I do not," said the Monkey; "and what is more, I insist on your telling me."

"Well, if you will 'ave it, you will 'ave it," said the Hawk. "Do you really suppose that there serpent thing will be content to sit next to that there Ring-dove when she'd rather be sittin' alongside of somebody else?"

"Somebody else?" said the Monkey. "Who on earth do you mean?"

"I mean you," said the Hawk. "You!"

"What!" screamed the Monkey. "Do you really mean she wants *me*? that I am her everlasting victim, her marked-down prey, and not the Ring-dove?"

"Certainly, you are. Didn't you know, really, Mister Jack?"

"'Enry," said the poor Monkey, now beside himself and pale with terror, "'Enry, the golden moment of your life has come.

Fly with me as fast as you can to Timbuctoo—I will *never* be her everlasting victim. Never ! "

And with that he gave a flying leap, right on the Hawk's back, and away they went, and were out of sight in the twinkling of an eye.

Ann came gliding back, all ready in her traveling skin, to go flying with Jack, but there was no Jack to be found. Imagine her dismay ! "He has escaped me for ever ! " she cried.

"Oh, don't cry, don't cry," whispered her Sprite. "I can't bear to see you unhappy. I can catch that clever, chattering Monkey for you, wherever he has gone. I am the Sprite of Immortal Life. Together we are invincible. No he-monkey, however clever he may be, can ever escape *us*." And it was true ; but the flight was to be a long and difficult one.

"Now, think quickly of someone to take us after him," said the Sprite. "Is there no bird in all the forest as fast as that He-hawk ? "

"Well, there is the Eagle," said Ann. "He's quite a friend of mine. Where is he, I wonder ? "

Just then the Eagle alighted on a tree-top above her.

"Hi ! " called out Ann. "Hi ! "

"How's that ? " said the Eagle.

"Take me to Timbuctoo ; I have important business there," said Ann.

"I'll do that," said the Eagle. "I'm some flyer, you know,

and I wager I can locate that He-hawk wherever he's got to. So you get right up, and off we'll go."

And she started on her perilous flight after that terrified He-monkey, Jack.

Now Jack and 'Enry had arrived in Timbuctoo, both of them overjoyed—Jack, because of his wonderful escape, and 'Enry, because of his wonderful flight. And just as they were preparing to enjoy themselves and have a really good time, the Hawk's far-seeing eye saw something in the distance that made him give his peculiar little whistle and take himself off.

"Good God!" groaned the Monkey, who had learned by now what that peculiar whistle meant. "Good God!" And as he looked up he was confronted by that inevitable female, Ann.

"I won't marry you, I won't marry you," blurted out the poor Monkey, not knowing in the least what a dangerous thing he was saying.

Ann was a bit amazed at the simplicity of her clever Monkey. "Why should you think I *want* to marry you, Jack?" she answered.

"I don't care whether you want to or not; you've got to marry Tavy."

"But I don't care for Tavy. He thinks I am a dove with angel's wings, and that bores me; but you know I am a serpent, and that fascinates me."

The poor Monkey felt his strength going. "You are a

hypocrite, and I hate hypocrites," he said, trying hard to make himself hate her.

" I must be a hypocrite for my future husband's sake," she answered.

" For my sake ?—I mean for his," said the Monkey hastily (furious with himself for having made such a blunder).

" Yes, for your sake," whispered Ann.

" Well, I can be a hypocrite, too," said the Monkey. " Your father appointed me your keeper, not your husband."

" I told my father to appoint you my keeper," said Ann, " so that I could bind you to me without frightening you too much."

" Oh ! " moaned the poor Monkey, " then I am lost. The trap was laid from the beginning."

" Yes," said Ann, " full of magic and power from the beginning, from our childhood, by my Sprite of Immortal Life."

" What, have you a Sprite, too ? " said Jack. " Why did you never tell me of that before ? "

" You never wanted to talk about me, Jack ; you only wanted to talk about yourself."

" She even knew that," groaned the Monkey. " But I will not marry you ! I will not marry you ! " he shrieked.

" Oh, yes, you will, you will."

" I tell you no, no."

" I tell you yes, yes."

" NO," thundered the Monkey.

At that dreadful "NO" poor Ann suddenly gave up hope and sank to the ground in despair.

The Monkey gazed at her weakness, and it was too much for him. "I do love you, I do love you, I was only fighting for my freedom."

"I can give you something better than freedom," she whispered.

"Oh, I know what you mean. It is your Sprite with her power of creating new creatures. I feel her power getting hold of me, too. Good God, is there a father's heart, too, as well as a mother's ? "

"Sometimes there is," she whispered.

"I am yours, then," said the Monkey, "and you are mine and the world is ours, oh, you snake, you snake," he cried, seizing her in his arms.

At that moment the other animals came running up.

"I have promised to marry Jack," said Ann.

"Yes, but I am not happy," protested Jack. "Ann looks happy, but she's only triumphant."

"Oh, you brute, Jack," said one of the animals. "Fancy an engaged animal saying things like that ! "

"Never mind him, dear," said Ann, looking up at the Monkey with pride and joy. "You go on chattering : I like it."

"Chattering ! That's all she sees even in me," said the poor Monkey, utterly crushed.

But he was caught, and that's all that matters, because this story is to show how the Sprite of Immortal Life creates new creatures.

PYGMALION

or, The Wizard and his Parrot

PYGMALION

or, *The Wizard and his Parrot*

THE Wizard was wise—but he knew nothing.
The Wizard was kind—but he cared nothing.
The Wizard did good—but he did nothing.
He was just himself.

And the Parrot, apparently, was only a dirty, stupid, squawking She-parrot; but the Wizard took her, and taught her, and turned her squawk into the most beautiful voice, and turned her into a most beautiful . . . but I mustn't tell you that until the end of my story.

When I said the Wizard was wise, but he knew nothing, I meant that he was wise about the things that didn't matter, and quite ignorant about the things that did matter ; I mean he had no manners, and manners matter a lot. . . . For instance, when the Wizard felt rude, he was rude, and when he wanted anything, he grabbed it, and when he didn't like anything, he said so ; he would never pretend, ever, he was just himself, and *sometimes* this made other people just *themselves* too. It was, in fact, because of his being just himself that made him able to turn that stupid, squawking Parrot into a most beautiful . . . but I mustn't tell you that, yet.

The Wizard was a wizard of sounds ; his ears were magical, he could hear things that nobody else could hear, and from the sounds that everyone made, he could tell exactly what part of the earth they came from, and no one could deceive him. He had a great, big magical flower, like the one we call a convolvulus, and that magic flower, which the Wizard of All Sound kept in his cave, could take in all the sounds that were made, and hold them, and let them out again whenever the Wizard wished ; and I wouldn't be surprised if that magical flower of the Wizard's was the beginning of our gramophone, it's so very like it.

But now, I really must begin at the beginning, or you will think this isn't a proper fairy tale.

Once upon a time there was a cold, rainy night, so cold and rainy that everyone was huddled together trying to get shelter, and everyone talked and quarrelled and scurried and worried and squawked and squeaked ; and the Wizard was there, in the midst of it all, collecting the sounds that everyone was making and writing them down in his book. There were Parrots and Cockatoos, a Sparrow, a Hen, and a Jackass—and a Toff. Now, a Toff is a man, who is, apparently, the exact opposite to our Wizard, for a Toff is very wise indeed about the things that matter ; he has the most beautiful manners, and is gentle and kind and never hurts anyone's feelings if he can help it—in fact, he is called a Gentle-man, and everybody in the world would know that he was a Gentle-man ; though everyone wouldn't

But the Wizard took her, and taught her, and turned her . . .

know that the Wizard was, too. Nevertheless, he was, but in a different way, as you will see.

Now, among all those squawking, squeaking birds there was a Sparrow twittering at the top of her voice at her brother, the Jackass. Aren't fairy tales funny? Fancy a Sparrow and a Jackass being brother and sister with a Hen for a mother! But if you come to think of it, it's not so funny after all ; haven't you ever called your brother a Jackass ?

Well, as I said before, the Sparrow and the Hen screamed at the poor Jackass to go out in the rain and find them a coach to go home in ; and so, of course, he had to go, and—*bang !*—he bumped right into Liza, the Parrot, knocking her over.

" Nah then, Jackass, mind 'ow yer go ! "

" Ee-aw ! " jeered the Jackass.

" Ee-aw, yerself," squawked the Parrot.

His mother, the Hen, who had been listening, hopped up to the Parrot at this. "However did you know that my son's name was Jackass ? " she asked in surprise.

" Only 'ad to look at 'im to know that ! " squawked the Parrot, cheekily. " Pick me up."

" Do no such thing, Mother ! " twittered the Sparrow.

" Pick me up, won't nobody pick me up ? " continued the Parrot. " Won't you pick me up, sir ? " she said, all soft like, turning to the Toff.

" Oh well ! I couldn't quite do that, you know ! " said the Toff, politely, " but here's something for you."

Just as the Parrot was about to accept, she felt a peck from one of the Cockatoos. "You be careful," he whispered, "there's a cop be'ind you takin' down every word ye're sayin'."

"Well! I ain't said nothing," squawked the Parrot.

"Oh, 'aven't you?" retorted the Cockatoo, "yer asked the Toff there to pick you up. Birds ain't allowed to talk to Toffs, you ought to know that."

"I ain't no bird, I'm a respectable Parrot, I am; don't you listen to 'im, sir!" she squawked, turning to the Wizard (for it was he). "He's a shameful Cockatoo bird! I didn't mean nothing. I ain't done nothing wrong! You'd never give a poor Parrot in charge . . ."

"Oh, shut up! Shut up!" said the Wizard. "Now I ask you, do I look like a cop?"

"Nao!" squawked the Parrot, cheekily, "yer look like nothin' on earth, but you just show me what you've writ abaht me."

The Wizard showed her all the weird sounds he had marked down.

"*Uh!*" said the Parrot, "I can't read that, it's not proper parrot talk. What does he say, Cocky?"

"He says," answered the Wizard, before Cocky had time to speak, "that you are a long way from home." (He could tell that from her sound.)

"Well! What if I am, what's it got to do with you? I've

as much right to be here as you 'ave ; you don't know where my home is, so there ! "

"Bird Lane," said the Wizard, coolly.

The Parrot was quite taken aback, for her home was in Bird Lane !

" 'Ere, 'ave you been followin' me abaht ? " she squawked, angrily.

" Sure, 'e 'as, 'e's sweet on you ! " said the Cockatoo.

" Step-nigh is where you come from," said the Wizard, turning to the Cockatoo.

" Hup the pole is where you belong ! " retorted the Cockatoo.

The birds and things all round roared at this. " You got 'im fair, you did ! 'E thinks we're all dirt under 'is feet. 'E wouldn't dare talk to the Toff that way ! "

" Oh ! wouldn't I just ! " said the Wizard coolly.

" Well then, sir," said the Toff gently, " will you tell me what I am ? "

" Army-cut ! " answered the Wizard, without a moment's hesitation.

" Right you are, sir ! However do you do it ? I congratulate you ! "

" Where on earth's that Jackass got to ? " shrieked the Sparrow. " I shall perish with cold if he doesn't come soon."

" Genteel ! " murmured the Wizard to himself.

" Mind your own business ! " screamed the Sparrow, shrilly ; " and don't dare to pry into *my* affairs."

"Oh ! do mind your manners, dear," clucked her mother, the Hen.

"Your Mother is Barnfowl, unmistakably," said the Wizard.

"How very curious !" chirped the Hen. "I was born and reared at Great Barnfowl."

"The devil you were !" chuckled the Wizard.

"Oh, 'e's balmy. Balmy from hup the pole !" said Cocky, and they all squeaked and squawked and screeched with laughter ; and, as it had stopped raining, they hopped, flew, and strutted off, leaving the Wizard alone with the Toff ; except for Liza the Parrot, who went on squawking and squawking in her stupid way.

"Stop that infernal row," thundered the Wizard, "or go home to roost !"

"Go 'ome ter roost yerself !" she retorted. "I've as much right 'ere as you 'ave."

"A creature who makes such horrible sounds has no right to be anywhere !" said the Wizard severely.

"Oh come, I say !" said the Toff, "isn't that going rather too far ?"

"I'll go still farther," said the Wizard who cared nothing. "I'll wager I could take that Parrot, making that stupid, squawking sound, a sound that will keep her a stupid, squawking Parrot as long as she lives, and in six months I could teach her to sound like a Princess. That's the sort of thing I do for a living.

I turn Grubs, moneyed Grubs, you know, into Princes, and they pay me handsomely for it."

"Well," said the Toff, "I am a student of sounds, myself, but mostly sounds from the East."

"Are you?" said the Wizard excitedly. "Do you by any chance happen to know Army-cut Pick-ring, Wizard of Sounds from the East?"

"I am Army-cut Pick-ring, Wizard of Sounds from the East. Who are you, sir, if I may ask?"

"I am the Wizard of All Sound."

"My dear sir!" said Army-cut, "I have come all the way from the East on purpose to meet you!"

"My dear sir, I was going all the way to the East, on purpose to meet you," said the Wizard excitedly. "It's like a fairy tale, our meeting like this. Come round to my place, and let's have a pow-wow."

The Parrot, seeing them move off, determined to make one last effort to get them to give her something. But she didn't have to, for the voice of God suddenly spoke to the Wizard—who was kind, but who cared nothing—and he flung her a handful of gold and silver and went on his way with Army-cut Pick-ring.

The Parrot, lost in amazement at the miracle that had happened to her, and, spying the Jackass, who at that moment arrived with the coach, calmly walked right up to it and hopped into it.

" Ta-ta ! Jackass ! " she squawked, " I'm going home in a coach, I am ! " and was out of sight in the twinkling of an eye, leaving the Jackass open-mouthed with astonishment.

" Well, I'm blowed ! " murmured the Jackass, lost in admiration ; " that bird flies high, and no mistake ! "

The next day, as the Wizard and Pick-ring were rapturously listening to the Magic Flower, Pick-ring quite speechless with wonder, the Wizard's slave suddenly appeared in the doorway, all ruffled and troubled.

" What's the matter with you, slave ? " grinned the Wizard. " You look as if you'd seen a ghost."

" Well, sir," said the slave, " to tell you the truth, that's just about what I have seen, for a dirty, squawking She-parrot is standing outside, demanding to see you, and says she won't go away until she has ! "

" Does she sound interesting, slave ? "

" Oh, no, sir ! " said the slave. " She has the most awful sound I ever heard, but—begging your pardon, as sometimes you do do such queer things . . ."

" All right," interrupted the Wizard, " bring her in. I'll show you how the Magic Flower takes in her sound, Pick-ring," he said. At that moment, to the Wizard's disgust, who should appear in the doorway, but Liza, the Parrot of the night before.

" Good Lord ! " said the Wizard, rudely, " I don't want you,

I heard all I want to hear of you, last night. Take her away, slave ! I don't want her."

" ' Ere, don't yer be so saucy ! " was the Parrot's amazing reply. " You don't know what I've come for yet. I've got gold and silver enough to buy you to teach me to talk genteel ; I know it's genteel, because I 'eard you say so to that helegant, harrogant Sparrow, I did."

The Wizard and Pick-ring were astonished at the unusual something about her.

" Look here," said Pick-ring, excitedly, " what about that wager of yours, that you could take her and teach her, and pass her off before the King and Queen as a princess ? I am willing to pay for the experiment—but I bet you can't do it ! "

" Done ! " said the Wizard, chuckling with delight. " Done ! We'll start at once. Take her away and clean her, slave."

" I won't be taken away and cleaned ! " screamed the Parrot, outraged. " I come from Bird Lane, I do, where the Cockatoos all treat me proper ! "

" Now then, we want none of your Bird Lane prudery here," shouted the Wizard. " You've got to learn to behave like a princess. Take her away and clean her, slave."

" I'll call a cop if you lays a 'and on me ! " squawked the Parrot. " You're no Gentle-man, you ain't ! "

Now nothing annoyed the Wizard so much as for anyone to

think he wasn't a Gentle-man, because he knew he was ; and he was too, but it would probably take a princess to find it out.

"Throw her out, slave ! " he shouted, furiously.

Pick-ring, who had been listening quietly to this rather vulgar row, now stepped forward. And with his most beautiful and gentle manner invited the Parrot to sit down. Never, in all her life, had anyone spoken to her like that ; never before had she felt as she did as she sank into the chair brought for her by Army-cut Pick-ring.

"What is your name ? " continued he, politely.

"Liza Do-nothing," she answered, all soft-like.

"Well, Miss Do-nothing."

"*Miss* Do-nothing." Liza's heart nearly stopped with the wonder of it all.

"Now, look here," interrupted the Wizard, "Liza doesn't understand all that gentleness. Give her orders, that's all she'll understand."

"Oh ! You great bully, you," squawked Liza. "You've no feelin' 'eart in you, you don't care for nobody but yourself. I'm off, I am ! "

"Have a cherry, Liza ? " asked the Wizard, craftily. He was beginning to enjoy himself with her.

"'Ow do I know wot's in it ? " retorted the Parrot. "I've 'eard of birds like me being doped by gentles like you ! "

"Pledge of good faith, Liza," said the Wizard, gallantly, cutting the cherry in halves, and popping one half into his own mouth, and the other into hers. The Parrot was secretly sur-prised and pleased at the way he was treating her, although his way was so different from Pick-ring's.

" Now, listen, Liza," said the Wizard. " You are to leave Bird Lane, and come and live here with Pick-ring and me, and be taught to speak beautifully, like a princess."

" Not genteel ? " said Liza.

" Genteel ? Good Lord, no ! That's not good enough for you."

" *Aoouuu !* . . ." Liza was dumbfounded.

" Stop that infernal row, and listen to me," continued the Wizard. " If you are a good bird, and behave yourself properly, you shall have lots of lovely cherries to eat, and a lovely place to sleep in, and lots of gold and silver, so that you can drive about in coaches. But if you don't behave yourself, you shall sleep among the black beetles, and be walloped by the slave. At the end of six months, Pick-ring and I will drive you to Court, and present you to the King and Queen as a beautiful princess. If the King finds out that you are not a princess, but only a cheeky, squawk-ing, stupid She-parrot, you will have your head chopped off as a warning to all other stupid, squawking, presumptuous She-parrots. Now, take her away and clean her, slave."

And so the Wizard had his way.

" I wonder," said Pick-ring, turning to the Wizard, " if you are a man to be trusted with a poor, defenceless bird."

"My dear Army-cut, is any man to be trusted with a poor, defenceless bird ? "

At that moment the slave reappeared at the door, more ruffled and troubled.

"Well, what's the matter now ? " inquired the Wizard.

"May I have a word with you, sir ? "

"Certainly ! What word would you like ? "

"Well, sir, it's a word *about* words, if I may say so, sir."

"A word about words ; what the devil do you mean by that ? "

"That's just what I mean, sir, that 'What the devil,' 'Which the devil,' 'Where the devil' . . ."

"Slave ! such language from your maiden lips ! "

"My maiden lips be blowed, sir ! "

"SLAVE ! ! " exclaimed the Wizard, quite aghast.

"Oh, it's not so bad for me to talk that way, as it is for you, sir, considering as how I know when I'm doing it, whereas you don't."

THE WIZARD WAS WISE, BUT HE KNEW NOTHING.

"I have come to say, sir," continued the slave, inexorably, "that now that you have a Parrot living in the house with you, you will have to mind how you behave, as she will naturally copy everything you do."

"But I never do anything I ought not to," said the Wizard, quite astounded at being told such things about himself.

"Well, sir, there's your habits."

" What's wrong with them ? " demanded the Wizard.

" Well, sir, you don't half dress yourself for your morning meal ; then you gobble everything off the same plate ; then you wipe your mouth on the table cloth . . ."

" STOP ! " thundered the Wizard.

" No, sir, I can't stop. You must listen to me, you can't rough-ride over everyone."

" *I* rough-ride over everyone ? " said the Wizard in amazement. " Why, I am the most kind, the most wise, the most . . ."

" Yes, I know all about that, sir ; but you don't know, sir ; you don't care, sir . . . Excuse me, there's someone at the door."

" The trouble has started already," said the slave, returning almost immediately ; " there's a scavenger outside saying you have his Parrot here."

" Show the blackguard up. We'll have some fun with him," said the Wizard, turning to Pick-ring. He certainly didn't care !

" Which of you two gentles is the Wizard of All Sound ? " demanded the scavenger, entering at that moment.

" I am," said the Wizard. " What do you want ? "

" I want my Parrot."

" Of course you do. Well, take your Parrot," said the Wizard, cleverly. The Wizard *was* wise, for he knew in a flash that the old blackguard didn't really want his Parrot at all, but had come to get gold and silver out of him. " You're her owner, aren't you ? " continued the Wizard. " Well, take her away at once, I don't want her."

The scavenger's face fell at the turn things had taken. He had not expected such cleverness from the Wizard ; but he wasn't going to be outdone.

" Now, listen 'ere," said he, craftily ; " you don't seem to understand the situation—and, I ask you, is it a proper situation for two gentles to have a bird living in the house with them— that's all I ask—is it proper ?—and what do I get for keeping my mouth shut ? "

" Jail ! That's what you'll get ! " thundered the Wizard, " for coming to try and get gold and silver out of me, by trying to frighten me with that kind of stuff."

" I never said a word about gold or silver, did I ? " demanded the scavenger.

" Then what did you come for ? " asked the Wizard, still pretending to be furious, but secretly chuckling with delight at the scavenger's all too natural talk.

" Well, what would a scavenger like me come for ? Be 'uman, guv'nor ! "

The Wizard burst out laughing. The scavenger had disarmed him completely with his utter shamelessness, and so he offered him five pieces of gold.

" . . . or shall I make it ten ? " he said, turning to Pick-ring.

" No," said the scavenger, to the Wizard's and Pick-ring's astonishment, " for if you gave me ten, I'd feel I ought to save it.

Give me the five, and I'll blow the lot in a couple of days. I am a good-for-nothing, that's what I am, and I enjoy it ! "

The Wizard roared with delight—never had he met anyone who was so just himself.

" 'Ello ! Wot 'ave we 'ere ? " exclaimed the scavenger, as the door opened and in walked a clean, brushed-up, radiant-looking bird. The scavenger cocked his eye at her, Pick-ring and the Wizard did, too. Liza (for it was she) stood there in all her natural glory.

" Garn ! All of yer ! " said she. " Wot yer starin' at ? "

" It's Liza ! " they all cried in amazement.

" Well, I reckon she'll be worth five gold pieces to you now, Wizard," said the wicked old scavenger, as he took his departure.

" Liza ! " said Pick-ring.

" Oh ! " said Liza, disappointed, " aren't you going to call me Miss Do-nothing any more ? It sounds so genteel ! "

" I beg your pardon, Miss Do-nothing."

Liza preened herself. " I shall want some brand new feathers now, I shall. These aren't good enough."

The Wizard winked at Pick-ring. " We shall have our work cut out for us."

" We shall," said Pick-ring.

But they had a wonderful time teaching Liza. She was so quick and clever, and faithfully copied everything the Wizard taught her, in her parrot-like manner. The Wizard was boundlessly proud of her, and thought he had taught her so perfectly that he wanted to show her off at one of his mother's parties. His poor, unsuspecting mother little knew what was in store for her and her guests, when one fine day her door opened and in walked her son.

" Oh, you must go away, dear," she said, " I have some guests coming this afternoon."

" Yes, I know," said the Wizard, " that's why I came."

" Oh, but you offend them all, dear."

" Can't help that, Mother, I've come on purpose. Three months ago a Parrot walked into my house, asking me to teach her to speak properly, and I have changed her from a dirty, stupid, squawking Parrot into a beautiful creature, with a lovely voice. I want to show her to you; you will be so proud of us both, Mother."

THE WIZARD WAS WISE, BUT HE KNEW NOTHING.

His mother was aghast, but it was too late to say anything. Her guests—a mother, her son, and her daughter—were beginning to arrive. The Wizard's mother introduced them. The Wizard stared at them all three in turn.

" I've seen you lot before, somewhere," he said, rudely. " Where the devil was it, I wonder ? " Then he began to remember the night when it was so cold and rainy. " Why, if it isn't the Hen, the Sparrow, and the Jackass ! " groaned the Wizard ; " what a beastly disappointment ! "

His mother and the poor Hen were aghast at his rudeness ; the Jackass, however, brayed with delight, and the Sparrow, thinking it all very new and exciting, said to him, coyly, " I think you are quite right to be just yourself, you know ! "

" Oh, do you ? " said the Wizard. Luckily, before he could say any more, Liza the Parrot walked gracefully into the room. Her beauty and distinction caused such a sensation that the whole company was speechless with wonder and admiration.

" What did I tell you, Mother ? " whispered the Wizard.

" How do you do ? " said the Parrot, graciously. She really was like a princess.

" Won't you come and sit here ? " said the Wizard's mother.

Then the Parrot began to talk, and the more she talked the less like a princess she became, and the more the Jackass and the Sparrow giggled, and the more the poor Wizard (who knew nothing) was delighted. But the Toff remained polite and gentle, as always.

" I am only a bird, you know," the Parrot was saying in her beautiful voice. " The Wizard picked me up, and I live with him ; it's the very devil sometimes, I can tell you. He certainly is up the pole, as Cocky said at the very beginning, for my owner, the old blackguard of a scavenger, turned up the next day, and the Wizard bought me from him for five gold pieces. That's the scavenger's job, you know, talking money out of people's pockets into his own. He blew the whole lot on drink, I'll be bound, the old blackguard ! "

At that the company could contain themselves no longer, and the Jackass exploded.

" What the devil are you laughing at ? " said the Parrot.

" The New Talk, you do it so well ! " he replied.

" If I do it so well, why are you laughing ? Have I said any-thing I oughtn't ? " asked the Parrot, uneasily.

" Oh, no ! " said everyone, hurriedly, trying to pretend that everything was all right.

" Well then, I can tell you a lot more things . . ."

" *Ahem !* " said the Wizard.

Liza knew that was her signal to go, so she rose gracefully, and wishing them all ' Good-bye,' swept out of the room.

" Isn't she lovely, Mother ? " said the poor Wizard, inno-cently. " Do you think the King and Queen will approve of her ? "

" You're surely not thinking of taking her to Court," said his mother, aghast.

" Certainly, I am. I have a bet on with Pick-ring that I can pass her off as a princess. I am the Wizard of All Sound, Mother. You can't deny that she speaks as beautifully as a princess."

" Well, dear, she *pronounces* her words as beautifully as a princess, but *what words !* "

" What's the matter with her words, Mother ? " demanded the Wizard ; " they're all right—I use them ! "

" That's just it, dear, you use them, and, being a Parrot, she has naturally copied you perfectly ; so, of course, she will never be fit for Court, as long as she lives with you."

" I'm afraid that's true," said Pick-ring, gently.

The poor Wizard was dumbfounded. He was accustomed to his mother and his slave criticising him, but, Pick-ring ! Could it really be true, after all, he wondered. Well he must win his bet, so he must take himself in hand. And, lo and behold, in another three months Liza the Parrot, Pick-ring, and the Wizard drove up in a coach to Court, to meet the King and Queen. And so, before a throng of criticising aristocratic eyes, did our beautiful She-parrot step out of her coach, walk up to the throne, and make her obeisance ; and not one pair of the criticising aristocratic eyes were able to pierce her disguise, so wonderfully had the Wizard and Pick-ring taught her. It had been a great day, and now it was all over, and they drove home together.

Yes, it was all over—for the Wizards. It had been a big day, and they were tired, and they said so, and they said they were glad it was over, and they went to bed without a word to the Parrot.

But what of the Parrot, the Princess, the She-thing ? It wasn't all over for her, it was only just beginning. If it was all over for the Wizards, what was to become of her ? Where was she to go ? What was she to do ? She began to feel slighted and hurt and angry, and there she sat—all alone, shaking with a rage and loneliness, such as she had never felt in all her life before. Hearing the Wizard outside the door, all her pent-up rage burst forth.

" What on earth's the matter with you, Liza ? " the Wizard asked in astonishment.

" You ! You ! " screamed the Parrot. " You, with your cold, unfeeling, selfish heart. You care for nobody but yourself. Now that I've won your bet for you, you don't care what happens to me ! " And she went for him with her claws.

The Wizard seized her coolly and flung her on the floor, where she lay, overpowered by his superior strength, her heart somewhat comforted, nevertheless ! She must go on enraging him—yes, she must, she must find out about him, how much he could feel, how much he could care, how much she could hurt him. Oh ! if she *could* only hurt him. How strange it was that a Parrot should have such human emotions !

But it made no difference to the Wizard, the Wizard who was just himself—who treated everyone alike, who didn't treat her like a She-thing, but treated her like himself. And because he didn't give her back the answers she expected, she became more and more furious, and goaded and hurt him more and more ; and when she saw that she *had* hurt him, she determined to leave his house, because she knew that would hurt him the most of all.

When the Wizard appeared next morning, he found his bird had flown. He was dismayed ; seizing his hat he and Pickring rushed over to his mother to tell her of his loss. But his mother wasn't going to help him ; she wanted him to find out for himself about She-things' hearts. So she teased him, and hid from him the fact that his Parrot had come to her and was safely upstairs all the time. But when his mother saw that she had teased him enough, she sent for the Parrot to come down. And the Parrot came down, hiding her triumphant, raging heart, which was now full of craftiness and power, and more like a princess's than ever. She addressed herself exclusively to Pick-ring, praising him for his gentleness and his tact, telling him that his own courtly manners had enabled her to become a princess and to win the Wizard's bet for him—because he was a Gentle-man, and he had always treated her as a princess.

"I shall always be a low, squawking Parrot to the Wizard," she said, "because he has always treated me as one."

"Liar !" burst forth the Wizard in a fury, "my manners are exactly the same as Army-cut's."

"No !" said the Parrot, "they are not ; for he treats a low, squawking Parrot as if she were a princess."

"And I," shouted the Wizard, "treat a princess as if she were a low, squawking Parrot !"

"I see," said she, scathingly, "just like the scavenger, the same to everybody !"

"Just so, Liza ; just ourselves !"

Liza felt somewhat nonplussed. "I don't care how you treat me as long as you treat me somehow," she faltered.

"I'm not going to alter myself for you, you presumptuous creature." He was goading her now, but quite unconsciously, he was brave and fearless and a match for anything and anybody. "You can come back and live with us or go to the devil, whichever you like ! " said he, coolly.

"What am I to come back for ? " said the Parrot, craftily.

"Just for the fun of the thing ! " answered the Wizard.

Now, I ask you, what could a She-thing make of that ? The Wizard was winning, she couldn't beat *him*, beat her wings against him as she would.

"I want kindness," she moaned, "I know I'm only a Parrot."

"You're only a fool ! " he retorted. "However, if you want someone to love you, and beat you, go back to Bird Lane. But, if you want to be a princess, you must *feel* like one, and be able to stand gentles being themselves to you."

"You only say that to be cruel," said the Parrot. "You know I can't go back to Bird Lane now, after having lived with you two gentles." (She had at last admitted he was a gentle !) "You think that you can insult me because I've got nowhere to go. But I'll soon show you that I have. The Jackass wants me, so there ! "

The Wizard was distinctly annoyed. "What ? " said he, crossly. "Is my beautiful handiwork to be wasted on a Jackass ? " (She was secretly pleased by that.)

"Very well then," she retorted, "I'll go and be a teacher."

"And what can you teach ? " asked the Wizard, scathingly.

"What you've taught me, *sounds* ! " said the Parrot, trium-phantly. "I'll go and offer myself as assistant to that other Wizard of Sound, your rival ! "

The Wizard was livid with fury, and made as if to lay his hands on her. "You dare call that impostor, that humbug, my *rival !* You'll teach him my discoveries, will you ? Let me hear you say that again, and I'll wring your neck ! "

"Wring away ! " said the Parrot in triumph. "I don't care what you do to me, I am independent now, I have you in my power ; and to think that a few moments ago I was only a common, stupid Parrot begging for your kindness, while now, *now*, I am your equal, I am . . ."

The miracle was happening—the parrot was turning into a woman, a beautiful, powerful woman, worthy of—

The Wizard who was wise, and who knew nothing ;

The Wizard who was kind, but who cared nothing ;

The Wizard who did good, but who did nothing ;

The Wizard who was just himself.

"By Jingo ! " said the Wizard, lost in admiration, "I like you like this ! "

"Oh! You're only making up to me, now that you have found out I'm not afraid of you, and can do without you," said she in triumph.

"Of course I am, you stupid idiot, for now that I've made

a woman of you, you and I and Army-cut can be three Wizards together, instead of two Wizards and only a stupid Parrot."

Then the Parrot understood ; Liza was herself at last—his equal—as he wanted her to be.

ARMS AND THE MAN

or, How the Bat lost her Wings, and, incidentally, how the Prince lost His, but Gained . . .

ARMS AND THE MAN

*or, How the Bat lost her Wings, and, incidentally,
how the Prince lost His, but Gained . . .*

IT happens now and again among a family of Rats that a Bat is born ; for a Bat is only a Rat with wings on and any Rat can grow wings if it wants to. And our Baby Rat did want to—she wanted to very much. She wanted to fly, to fly away from the grubbiness of the earth, and dwell in a castle in the air with her Prince, her brave, strong, beautiful Prince ; and they would dwell there together for ever and ever, in beauty, wonder, and joy.

That was her dream, and she believed in her dream, in her Prince, and in the wonder and joy and beautifulness of everything. Until it happened one night—one fateful night— that a Rat climbed up the walls of her castle, got in at her window, and shattered her dreams for ever and ever, bringing her to earth with her castle tumbling about her ears, did that common or garden, cowardly, sensible young Rat, who for evermore will be known as the Lollipop—serve him right. And this is how it happened!

Now Rats are a grubbing, scratching, fighting lot, anyway, and so there was a fight on—a war, they called it, to make it sound grander—a big war, too, to those who were in it, but quite unimportant to those who were not ! What it was about, nobody knew—nobody ever does—but, nevertheless, there was a war on—a beautiful, noble war—and everybody was killing everybody else in a beautiful, noble manner. And the beautiful, noble Prince was in it. And the Bat lay in her castle dreaming dreams of the wonder and glory of it all !

When, hark ! her mother was calling her.

"My child, news ! great news ! there has been a victory won by your Prince—a splendid, noble victory. He is the hero of the hour and the idol of the Army."

"Oh ! " cried the Bat, springing up, "is it really true ? My dreams aren't dreams after all then, they are real, my Prince is a real Prince, my castle in the air is a real castle, and I am a real Princess ! What unspeakable joy, what happiness ! "

And her mother went on to tell her how her Prince had defied all the silly rules of war, taken the law into his own hands, and charged the enemy, making them run away like the rats that they were.

But before they had time to rejoice any further, the slave came in to tell them that they were ordered to close all the windows and doors, as the enemy were on the run, with the Prince and his Rats after them, and that there might be danger and shooting. The Bat, wishing her mother good-night, retired to her couch in her flimsy attire to dream her dreams of wonder and joy, leaving her window open.

It happened one night . . . that a Rat . . . got in at her window

Bang !—a shot rang out !—the fateful shot ! And the next minute a Rat scrambled up the walls of her castle and got in at her window—the Rat who was to shatter her dreams for ever and ever, and bring her to earth with her castle tumbling about her ears.

They stared at each other.

" I'm in danger," said the Rat, desperately. "If I am caught, I shall be killed, and I don't intend to be killed if I can help it," said he curtly, locking the door of her room and putting the key in his pocket.

The Princess drew herself up proudly. How different was the behaviour of this common, cowardly creature, running away from the battle and forcing his way into her room, from that of her noble, chivalrous Prince !

" Rats are afraid of death, I know that," she said, contemptuously.

" Of course they are," retorted the Rat briskly—he hadn't wasted his time growing wings and dreaming dreams and make-believing, not he ! He believed in what he could see, and in seeing what he could, and in living as long as he could ; he wasn't going to die if he could help it, not he, and he told her so straight. " So, if you let anyone in on me . . ." he continued, dangerously.

" You will shoot me," said she, proudly. " And how do you know I am afraid to be shot ? " That was a poser for the Rat, with his common or garden ideas ; for he could see quite well that she wasn't afraid—to be shot. But surely there must be *something* she feared.

And then he caught sight of her flimsy attire, and, being the common little Rat that he was, he decided what to do. . . . The Princess, guessing what was in his mind, darted for her cloak, to cover herself up with. The Rat, however, was too quick for her. Seizing it himself, he tauntingly told her that he would keep her cloak so that she would take care not to let anyone come in and see her without it !

The Princess gazed at him speechless. Never had she imagined that anyone could be so unspeakably unchivalrous. Her rage and scorn knew no bounds.

" You—Rat—you ! " she cried in disgust. And then a strange thing happened.

There was a knock at the door, and the Rat, believing that all was up with him, suddenly dropped the unchivalrous manner he had (sensibly !) adopted, and became considerate and friendly.

" Here's your cloak, wrap yourself up in it, quick ! " he whispered. " They're coming in—I'm trapped."

" Oh, thank you, thank you," said the Bat, quite surprised that the common little creature had some princely feelings in him after all.

" I will help you," said she. " Hide ! "

It was not a moment too soon ; in rushed the Rats in

search of him. But they didn't find him, and out they went, leaving the Bat and the Rat alone once more.

The Bat looked at him. What a strange creature he was, unlike anything she had seen before. He had no wings, of course, but yet . . . " Here's your pistol to defend yourself with," said she, almost softly !

" I can't defend myself with that thing," he said, laughing at her ; " it's not loaded. I never load it in war, I fill it up with lollipops instead. I finished the last one yesterday, and I am starving. I suppose you haven't got any to give me, have you ? "

The Bat couldn't believe her ears. " Lollipops ? " she gasped. A soldier filling up his pistol with lollipops ! She nearly swooned. (I told you he was going to shatter her dreams for ever and ever.)

Oh, yes ! she had some lollipops, and she would like to stuff them down his throat and choke him with them, too ! She rose contemptuously, and, seizing the box, flung them at him in scorn.

But the beautiful, noble scorn was wasted ; for he just helped himself, and ate up the lollipops to his heart's content, thanking her cheerfully for saving his life once more !

" *Ugh !* " said the Princess, snatching the empty box from him and flinging it away. Never had she conceived of such a despicable little worm. If she could only shame him or goad him into showing some pride or courage or something that she was accustomed to ! But nothing could shame him ! That's what puzzled her. What was he made of ? Why was he so different ? Why did she bother with him ? Ah, why ?

"The noble Prince who won the great victory over you does not stuff *his* pistol up with lollipops," said she, tauntingly.

"No, he's too much of a Bat to do anything so sensible ! "

"Too much of a Bat "—what could he mean ?

"Take care," said she, warningly. "You are speaking of the Prince to whom I am betrothed."

"God bless my soul ! If you are betrothed to him you should have seen him in the charge," said he, chuckling to himself.

"Oh ! " cried the Princess in a fever of joy and wonder. "Did you really see him ? Tell me, oh, tell me about him."

"All right, I will," said he, mischievously.

"Have you ever seen Rats on horseback, charging each other, Princess ? "

"No," said she, breathlessly.

"Well, first one comes, then two or three, and then the rest all together in a bunch."

"Yes, yes," cried the Princess in rapture. "First one, the winged hero, the Bat ! "

"Yes," said the Rat, drolly, "the Bat ! You should have seen the poor creature pulling at his horse ! "

"Pulling at his horse ? Whatever did he do that for ? " asked she in amazement.

"It was running away with him, of course. You don't

suppose he *wanted* to get there first, and be killed, do you ? " said he, severely. " He can't be quite such a Bat as all that."

The Princess gazed at him, speechless. What *could* a She-thing make of such a creature ? What on earth could he mean ? She couldn't help thinking it sounded sensible—but how low and unchivalrous to be sensible in war !

" You cannot deny, sir," said she, regaining her dignity with a mighty effort, " that my noble Prince has done a brave and valiant deed, and has gained a glorious victory over you."

" Brave and valiant," said the Rat in surprise, " to gallop a lot of Rats into the jaws of the cannon to be exterminated if the cannon happens to go off ? "

" But they weren't exterminated, and the cannon didn't go off," said the Princess, triumphantly. " So what do you make of that ? "

" He only gained a victory," said the Rat, crossly, " because our silly creatures sent the wrong stuff, and we couldn't get our cannon to go off. No doubt the Prince knew that, and knew he was doing a safe thing," continued the Rat, chivalrously trying to spare her feelings and make the Prince out to be a proper, sensible soldier, fighting in a proper, sensible way (if there is such a thing).

" Do you mean to infer, then, that my gallant, glorious be-trothed is a pretender, a make-believe ? " said she, now beside herself with rage at this new insult.

The poor little Rat gave it up, it was no good ! He couldn't knock any common sense into her, and he was so tired, he hadn't closed his eyes for days, so he just curled himself up on her bed and went to sleep.

The Princess gazed upon him in amazement. She couldn't, however, prevent her raging heart melting at the sight of him —he looked so defenceless. "Poor creature," she murmured to herself, "poor, dear, strange creature!"

Her mother, happening to hear these very unusual words issuing from her daughter's room, entered. There, to her astonishment, she saw her proud, arrogant daughter gazing on a strange Rat who was lying asleep on her bed.

What on earth could be the meaning of it? She commanded her daughter to explain. But her daughter couldn't even explain it to herself, let alone to her mother—for there is an imp inside all of us that gets its way in spite of everything and everybody—and the imp was binding the Bat to the Rat, whatever her mother or anyone else might say.

The war was over, the Prince would be returning. The Princess watched and waited. At last he came. She flew to him. "My hero," she murmured in ecstasy, "you have made my dreams come true. Your prowess in battle, your victory over the enemy have made your name immortal." The Princess was back in her castle-in-the-air with her gallant, glorious Prince!

But, alas, her bliss was short-lived, for at that moment, who should come in but that little Rat of a slave.

Catching sight of her out of the corner of his eye, the Prince instantly came down to earth. The Bat, wishing to remain in heaven, and out of sight of the slave, flew away, telling the Prince to await her. The Prince eyed the slave—she was a pretty creature.

Now, the slave dreamed dreams, and built castles, too, but not in the air ! She built hers on the earth, out of the clay, and she had seen the clay in the feet of the Prince. The Bat saw only his wings. That Rat of a slave desired the Prince ; and the Prince desired—he knew not what ! He was a Prince, and his Bat was a Princess—they both had wings to soar, and dreams to dream—but his feet were of clay, and they dragged him down. He desired to dance on earth with the slave ; he also desired to soar on high with the Princess. Which did he desire most ? Ah, that he did not know !

" Have you tried to fly, slave, to soar in the skies ? "

" No, sir," said she, demurely, looking down ; " I haven't."

" It's tiring, of course, to keep up all the time. One feels the need of a change after it. Come, dance with me, slave," said he, seizing her in his arms and pressing her to him. (The earth was warmer than the sky !)

The slave, however, was not to be caught so easily. " Bats are all alike," said she, scornfully, " in spite of their wings and their soarings ; here are you, dancing the earth with me behind the Princess's back, and there is she, dancing the earth with her

Rat behind yours. It shows how little either of you really care ! "

The Prince was staggered. He was being brought to earth with a vengeance ! " You common little clod of clay ! " said he, pushing her away from him in rage and disgust, " how dare you speak so of my beloved ? "

But the slave didn't mind what he called her, now that she'd found out that there was some of the same common clay in him !

Poor Prince ! He was neither a Bat nor a Rat. What was he ? And the slave was no slave, either, and the Lollipop was no lollipop, and this is no fairy tale ! For fairy tales are make-believe, and no one is allowed to make-believe in this tale, nor dream dreams, nor build castles, nor love—at least, not in a Bat's way. For when a Rat falls in love with a Bat it must bring its loved one to earth, and plant it firmly on its feet, and open its eyes—for a Bat, you know, is blind.

And this is what the slave would do for the Prince, and the Lollipop for the Princess.

Now, the Lollipop, who had returned to his army, wanted to have another look at the Princess (there's a common or garden way of thinking of one's best-beloved !—but anyway, that's the way he did think), he wanted to have another look at her ; so back he scampered to her home. Her mother, however, spied him in the distance—she didn't want a Rat for a son-in-law, not she ; she wanted a Prince. So she flew at him and tried to beat him back ; but the imp was on his side. The Princess's father and the Prince, who had known the Rat in the war, came out at that very moment, and they welcomed him joyfully as their friend the enemy, and then, who should appear but the Princess herself ! No sooner did her eyes light on the Rat than her heart went bounding, and before she knew what she was saying, she cried : " Why, if it isn't my Lollipop ! "

Imagine the amazement of her father and her betrothed, and the consternation of her mother ! There was a chilly, stilly silence. The Lollipop never turned a hair ! The Princess, realising her blunder, and being full of craftiness, turned to her father and said sweetly :

" My mind is full of lollipops to-day, Father, for I've been making some all the morning ! I hope you didn't think that I meant *you* were a lollipop, Rat," said she, demurely, looking at him out of the corner of her eye.

" I assure you I did," said he, feeling mighty glad he'd come to have another look at her. "Your explanation is a relief ! "

Then they all asked him to stay—all except the Bat's mother —she wanted him to go, but he wasn't going, not he !

And so the Bat and the Rat were together once again ! They looked at each other—they liked each other better than ever. They did not say so, not they ! The Bat was betrothed to her Prince.

" If the Prince finds out about you, Rat, he will challenge you to fight," said she, craftily.

"Don't tell him, then," said the Rat, in that provokingly sensible way of his.

"That's all very well for you, Rat" (she was trying to provoke him into saying something interesting, the wicked little she-devil !), "but for me, it means deceiving my hero and bringing a lie into our castle of dreams, though I don't suppose you can understand that, Rat," said she, condescendingly. The Princess was up in the air again ! The Rat gazed at her. He could understand only too well, and he jolly well wanted to let her know how well he did understand ; he felt that his moment had come. He gazed at her again. There was his Bat, his beautiful Bat, up in the air, fluttering her wings in an ecstasy of make-believe—a very entrancing sight, no doubt, but no good to him ! For what was the use of her being up in the skies when he wanted her down by his side ? He took a shot at her . . .

"I am not going to have you trying to make-believe that you've never told a lie before in all your life, Bat," said he, daringly. "I am a very truthful fellow myself, and a lie or two wouldn't last me a whole morning ! So come down to earth and be sensible."

The Bat stopped, stared, amazed and horrified.

"Do you mean to imply that I, a Princess, a Bat, tell lies like you or any other common or garden Rat ? "

"Of course I do," answered the Rat imperturbably. "Why not ? "

"Why not ? ? Why not ? ? ?"

She gazed at him, gazed into those eyes that saw through her, that bereft her of her wings, her glory. And what did she see in them ? Nothing but admiration ! ! !

She couldn't believe it, she was nonplussed. She hesitated. She trembled, she fell, crashing to earth by his side ! How natural it felt, down there beside him, how safe. Well, after all, why not ? She looked at him shyly : "How did you find me out, Rat ? I have made-believe all my life, and everyone has really believed ! My Prince believes, he and I could dwell in our castle in the air for ever and ever and ever."

"Are you sure of that, Princess ?" asked the Rat.

The Bat looked at him quickly, "Do you mean . . . ? Oh ! if I thought . . . "

The Rat didn't say any more—he knew enough not to . . . Oh, bother, he knew everything. She looked at him again. There he was, cheery, confident, beaming at her, waiting for her. Oh, he was irresistible !

"Tell me how you found me out," she whispered.

"With these," said he, pointing to his eyes.

"Oh," said the Bat, "I see ! . . ." So he had opened her eyes at last !—winged her, won her, and made her his. She had become a Rat, a common or garden Rat.

The Rat looked on at the metamorphosis of his beloved, feeling very powerful and happy.

"And now," said he, masterfully, "tell me to whom you have given yourself . . ."

"To my Lollipop . . ." said she, shyly; "to my sweetheart, my sweetie."

And the Prince got his clod of common clay.

And they all lived happily for ever and ever. And this *is* a fairy tale after all.

MRS WARREN'S PROFESSION
or, Love Birds in a Cage

MRS WARREN'S PROFESSION
or, Love Birds in a Cage

ONCE upon a time there was a common old goose slaving away in a common old barn for a bare living, and she had four offspring. Two of them were ugly—ugly and stupid— and had to work hard, ever so hard, harder even than their poor old goose of a mother, who, to tell you the truth, wasn't quite such a goose after all—for the next time she picked a better father for her offspring—she picked an aristocratic, gay young cock, whose offsprings took after him, and grew up to be two good-looking, gay young Birds, and their names were Lizzie and Kitty. Lizzie was the aristocrat of the two—but both were beautiful, and their beauty bound them together ; they scorned the ignorant, ugly, stupid fowls of the barnyard and would have nothing to do with them. And so when a chance came to Lizzie to get away from them altogether, she took her chance and got off.

The wise old Owl shook his head and warned Kitty that her beautiful sister would come to an unbeautiful end, and did his best to prevent her from following in Lizzie's footsteps. He found her some work, and sent her away to slave and slave. It chanced, however, that one cold winter's night a gay young

Bird, decked in gorgeous feathers, and as happy as a Bird can be, suddenly appeared before her.

Kitty stared in amazement, for lo ! it was her sister Lizzie, but a Lizzie who had learned what's what.

" Whatever has happened to you ? " gasped poor, tired, worn-out Kitty. " How is it you have grown so gay and so much more beautiful ? "

Lizzie looked at her sister and spoke to her thus :

" Kitty, you are beautiful too, much too beautiful to work and drudge and wear out your beauty in this manner. You must not remain a goose any longer, you must come away with me, and do what I do, and think what I think, and be what I am, for I am a Love Bird, and have learned many things. I have learned that there is a creature in the world called Man, and that Man loves beauty and will pay for it. So come away, Bird, come away ! The world is full of this creature Man, who'll pay ! "

So Lizzie took her sister away with her, Lizzie who had learned what's what. And they had not far to go, for when you are on the look-out, the creature Man, who pays, is everywhere ; at least so young and beautiful Birds like Lizzie and Kitty find. But Lizzie knew that it wasn't enough to be young and beautiful—she had seen young, beautiful Birds getting nowhere ; she knew, for instance, that one could get nowhere without gold, and that gold does not flow in by itself—it has to

The creature Man came to gaze on them, and take pleasure in them

be dug for hard, with eyes all soft-like, dug for all the time out of the creature Man, who pays. And so she dug hard, all the time, with eyes all soft-like, and taught her sister Kitty to do likewise. And what they dug for they kept and saved. But it was very hard work.

"Why should we go on digging all our lives ? " said Lizzie one day. "Let us not work so hard ourselves ; let us rather go out and buy with the gold we have saved a cage wherein we will lure other young and beautiful Birds like unto ourselves, who shall, in their turn, lure unto themselves the creature Man, who pays. We will make gain out of them, and life will not be so hard for us ! "

Kitty thought over what her sister said, and found it very good. And so they bought the cage (in foreign parts) and filled it with young and beautiful Love Birds, and the creature Man came to gaze on them, and take pleasure in them, and buy them, and pay Lizzie and Kitty for them. And they prospered, and Lizzie and Kitty went on saving and saving.

And it came to pass when Lizzie had saved enough that she took counsel with herself and decided that she would give up keeping Love Birds. She would go and dwell in splendour and contentment among the Peacocks of the realm. So, shaking the gold dust off her feet, she departed from that kind of life for ever.

But Kitty was different. She didn't want to give up. She enjoyed keeping Love Birds. She also enjoyed the creature Man, who pays. She had found a special one of her own—a Baron he was, and a crafty old cock at that. He and Kitty got together and bought more cages, and got more Love Birds to put in them, and more creatures to pay for them, and made more and more gold.

Now Kitty had a reason for wanting this gold. She had an offspring—her name was Vivie ; and Kitty loved her Vivie as much as her nature would allow—which was a lot in her way—but, alas, it was a goose's way.

Kitty was proud of her offspring, for her offspring took after Lizzie, and was haughty and wise and strong. And Kitty wanted the gold to spend on her, to train her. She did not want her Vivie to slave or save, or to be a goose or a Love Bird as she and Lizzie had had to be. Not she ! She wanted her Vivie to be a care-free, happy butterfly, to be able to flutter and bask in the garden of life, decked in the most brilliant of hues. Her Vivie must shine and dazzle and pick for herself the Flower of Youth, and mate with him, and live in the sunshine for ever.

That is what Kitty dreamed of, that is what she slaved for, and that is what she *bungled,* through being a goose, as you will see.

Vivie was sent to be trained. She hardly ever saw her mother ; her mother was busy looking after the cages, the Love Birds, and the pay.

And Vivie grew up, not in the butterfly way that her mother dreamed of, but in her own way, which turned out to be more of a silkworm's way ; for Vivie was a worker ; she spun and wove brilliant things certainly, but not brilliant things to deck her body with, but to deck her mind ; useful things, things she could turn into gold—should she ever need to. And so she learned to rely on herself, to think her own thoughts, to be her own self, and Vivie and her mother grew very far apart indeed.

" I am coming to see you, my love," wrote her mother when Vivie had finished her training, " and I am bringing with me the Baron, who wants to see the little Vivie he has heard so much of." And so the gay old Bird, Vivie's mother, and the crafty old cock, her partner, appeared upon the scene.

Vivie took one look at the Baron. Simple little Silkworm that she was, she was wise enough to know a crafty old cock when she saw one. The crafty old cock was not so wise ! No busy, independent young Silkworm had ever come his way before. Fluttering Love Birds digging for gold, with eyes all soft-like, were more in his line ; and because he had always had the gold, he had always had his way with them. The Silkworm was something new and different, and the jaded old cock just wanted something new and different. He was to get it, too, in a way he didn't expect ! He was going to find out that the creatures who can pay can't buy everything.

Now, there was a gay He-butterfly who loved that busy little Silkworm with all his loving heart, but alas ! he was a Butterfly, and how *can* a busy little She-thing love an idle little He-thing, however loving he may be ? The Butterfly hovered around.

He had spotted the crafty old cock, he had also spotted the gay old Bird (Vivie's mother), had that astute little fellow ; there wasn't much that escaped him ! He began to feel that his Vivie might need his protection some day.

"I shouldn't encourage that young Butterfly of yours, Vivie, my child," said her mother, in her most beautiful motherly fashion.

But Vivie had been brought up otherwise, and that beautiful motherly (old) fashion could play no part in her independent young life. "Yes," she said coolly, "I am afraid he is only a Butterfly ; but what about that crafty old cock of yours, what about him ? "

The old Goose could hardly believe her ears—how dare her offspring speak to her mother so ? Her mother must not put up with it, she must tell her so at once.

"You will have to make up your mind to the crafty old cock, as you call him," she said firmly, "now that we shall be together."

"Together ? " said the Silkworm in amazement. "You and I, Mother ? " she continued, quite taken aback.

"Of course," said her mother, determinedly. "We are mother and daughter, aren't we ? "

"Yes, but surely you don't think that my way of living will suit you ? "

Never in all her life had the old Goose heard of a daughter's way of life. A daughter's way of life was what her mother decided for her, so it was, and she would let her daughter know it, so she would. And then the poor old Goose made her first blunder.

"Hold your tongue," said she, rudely, "you don't seem to know to whom you are talking."

"No," answered the Silkworm, steadily (hiding her anger and disgust at her mother's rudeness, in her cool, aristocratic way). "No, I do not know. Who are you? What are you?"

What blood-curdling words for a mother to hear from her own offspring! The poor old Goose nearly fainted.

"I am your mother," she wailed, pitifully.

"Are you?" continued the Silkworm, mercilessly. "Then if you are my mother, who is my father?" That was a poser for an old Bird, like Vivie's mother, and no mistake!

"Who is my father? Who is my father?" They were words that the poor old Goose had dreaded for years to hear, and, horrible to relate, she could not answer them—she could not tell her offspring who her father was—for she did not know herself!

"I can't tell you that," she faltered.

"Can't tell me, Mother?" cried the Silkworm in horror. "Then how do I know that I am not the offspring of that crafty old Baron?"

"No, no," said the old Bird hastily, thankful to be able to reassure her daughter on that point. "No, no, it's not him. I am certain of that at least."

What blood-curdling words for a daughter to hear from her mother ! When the dreadful meaning of them dawned on her, her blood ran cold. But the brave little creature showed no sign of her misery and horror. " I think it's time you went to roost, Mother," was all she said.

But the old Bird was angry, angry with herself for letting the truth slip out, and angry with her daughter for her cold, superior attitude, and—common old thing that she was—she determined to make her offspring show her feelings. She wasn't going to let her hide inside that cocoon she had spun and woven for herself. Not she ! She would drag her out into the mire and bring her pride to the dust, she would ! And so Kitty began from the beginning to tell her beautiful, proud daughter what she'd sprung from : how her grandmother was a common old Goose slaving away in a common old barn ; how she had two ugly ducklings who had worked and slaved and got nowhere ; how she and her sister determined not to do the same ; how Liz got off one night and learned what's what ; how she had taught her sister what she had learned ; how they both determined that even that was not good enough ; how they had kept Love Birds in cages for Man to come and gaze at and take pleasure in and pay for ; how she and Liz had saved all the gold, and how Liz had now gone to live in splendour and contentment among the Peacocks of the realm !

The story was exciting, and the old Bird had enjoyed telling it. The Silkworm, courageous little thing that she was, couldn't help being impressed by it.

"You are a wonderful old Bird, Mother, and no mistake," she said ; "but do you really mean to say that you are not ashamed of the life you have led ? "

"No, my child," answered her mother, "I am not ashamed. Of course I have to pretend to be—the creatures of the world expect it of you ; but I am not ashamed—I have not harmed anyone ; I have treated my Love Birds better than I was treated —and some of the creatures have taken the Love Birds as mates, and live happily with them."

"And do you really mean to say, Mother, that if we had no gold now, you would not rather have me slave and save and get nowhere than become a Love Bird ? "

The Silkworm was sure that when it came to herself, her own daughter, her mother would think differently. But, to her amazement, the old Bird was true to her guns to the bitter end.

"Of course not," she thundered. "What sort of mother do you take me for ? "

The Silkworm was thrilled with her mother's courage, and felt nearer to her in that moment than she could ever have imagined possible.

The Butterfly, hovering around, saw it, and it made his heart sick. He was a worldly little fellow, and knew, better than the Silkworm could ever know, what that gay old Bird's life had been, and what she really was, and he knew that Vivie would never, never, be able to stand her old blackguard of a mother. He tried to tell her so, but she would have none of it ; she would stand by her mother, who had slaved and saved for her. It was only right !

But a rose cannot grow with garlic ; nor can the adder live with the dove ; nor will the wheat be garnered with the tares ; each must gain his own award and not another's.

Now, the gay old cock had made up his mind ; he wanted something new and different—he wanted to mate—and who could be more suitable than the offspring of his old partner ? So, spying her basking in the sunshine with that He-butterfly of hers, he thought his time had come. Up he strutted, and, dismissing the contemptible little Butterfly (as he thought), proceeded to entrap the Silkworm.

But even a worm will turn, yes, even a silkworm !

" I am an old cock, and a crafty old cock at that," began the Baron, craftily, thinking he was being very clever and impressive (and fascinating, too, no doubt).

" Yes, I don't doubt your word," answered the Silkworm.

The Baron cocked his eye. Was it said sweetly ? " Nice fellow, that young Butterfly of yours," he continued, cleverly. " Pity he flutters around so—not the way to lay by any store, is it ? Now, I've laid by a pretty good store. I'm rich and powerful, and I want a mate, and—the fact is, I want you ! What do you say ? " This he said with a dazzling smile and a magnificent strut. (Who could resist him ?)

Up he strutted

The Silkworm could ! She eyed him coolly. "I'm much obliged to you, Baron, but I'd rather not."

"Rather not ? " The old cock was decidedly nonplussed—but he needn't take ' no ' for an answer. He had plenty of ways of compelling that young Silkworm to his will ; in fact, her independence tickled his fancy. After all, she was something new and different. She was in his power, too. He could tell her all about her disgraceful old mother, and he would.

"I've been a very good friend to your mother," he began, "and I've given her a lot of money for her business."

"Do you mean that you and my mother were in the business together ? " said she, in horror and amazement. "Take care, for I know what my mother's business was."

"*Was*," said the old Baron, cruelly, "*is*."

"Do you mean that my mother still——" The poor little creature covered her face in shame. That was the end of everything. She would go away and hide—hide and spin and weave by herself for the rest of her life, for she would never touch another drop of her mother's tainted gold.

She turned to go, but the Baron wasn't going to let his prey get away from him like that, not he ! He seized her brutally in his beak.

The Butterfly was only waiting for that. He hadn't gone away. He'd been fluttering around, and now, with his antennæ full of poison, he flew at the Baron.

The Baron, realising his danger, and that all was up, thought discretion was the better part of valour, and took himself off like the bedraggled old Bird that he was, spitting venom as he went.

But the venom didn't poison them, they took good care of that.

But Vivie was crushed ; she would go and hide—hide away and work for ever, and she, too, went off as fast as her legs would carry her, leaving her poor Butterfly lost in amazement and dismay.

When the old Goose heard that Vivie had disappeared, she was very concerned and waddled off to find her. The Butterfly warned her not to (he knew !), but the old Goose would not listen, and she went stupidly on till she found her offspring, and *then* went stupidly on. She wasn't a Goose for nothing !

"I am glad you've come, Mother, for I want to tell you once and for all that my mind is made up. You and I must part ; you must go your way and I will go mine, for we have nothing in common. Good-bye."

"Good-bye ? " the poor old Goose couldn't believe her ears —couldn't believe that her own offspring, whom she had slaved and saved for, could leave her like this—her own mother ! Oh, no, it could not be, it was not natural—thought the poor old mother in the beautiful motherly old fashion. But the Silk-worm was not blinded by any fashion ; she spun her own thoughts, and wove her own life, and made her life suit, did that wise little creature in her infinite wisdom.

But her mother had never really spun her own thoughts nor woven her own life—had never been herself, and now she was to pay the price.

"You can't mean what you say—we're mother and daughter! And I want my daughter. Who's to look after me when I am old?" cried the old Bird, querulously. "You've no right to refuse to do your duty as a daughter."

"Your duty as a daughter!" The fat was in the fire. The motherly old fashion was out with a vengeance! The Silkworm had only been waiting for that.

"Look here, Mother, I am not going to sacrifice my life for a few of your cheap tears."

"Cheap tears!" To think that she should live to hear a mother's tears called cheap! Now she would let her daughter have it! And so the real, true nature of Kitty, the common old Bird, came out at last.

"Listen to me, you wretched worm, you," hissed the old Goose, beside herself with passion. "Do you know what I'd do with you if I had you as a baby over again? Would I slave and save and shower gold upon you, and bring you up to lead your own life and be your own self, and have everything your own way, and despise and spit on your old mother? No, I wouldn't. I'll tell you what I would do. I'd bring you up in one of my own cages, so I would, to be a Love Bird, so I would, for the creature Man to come and gaze on you, and have pleasure in you, and buy you and pay me handsomely for you, I would.

Oh," she said wildly, quite beside herself, " I'll never do right again as long as I live. I'll do wrong, nothing but wrong, and I'll prosper on it."

" That's right, Mother, be yourself—it's the only way ! That's why I'm leaving you—because you lead one life but believe in another."

And it was true, though the poor old Goose didn't believe it. She brooded and brooded for ever on the injustice of every-thing—just as we do—but there can't be any injustice. We bring to ourselves just what we are.

So now the courageous young Silkworm is spinning and weaving her life alone. But at least she is free—at least she is not in a cage.

THE DOCTOR'S DILEMMA
or, Come into the Garden

THE DOCTOR'S DILEMMA

or, Come into the Garden

"COME into the garden, all you who suffer and are sick ; for there shall you find your heart's desire ; your bodies shall be made whole, and your hearts glad, and great shall be your rejoicing."

Is there a mortal who could resist such a call ? Is there a creature who could remain outside ? No ! So we stray into the garden. And once we stray there we stay there, for it is pleasant to cast our burdens upon others who have promised to banish them for evermore—promised ! And we answer the call and we stand at the gate and knock ! And the gate is opened, and we behold the Healers.

Now the healers in the Magic Garden are manifold and their name is legion. But for the moment we are only concerned with the Thistle, the Rose, the Shamrock, the Sword-grass, the Tulip (pronounced *Ju-lip*), the Deadly Nightshade, the Ragged Robin, and last, but not least, the Poppy. Now each of these healers has his own particular way of working his magic : the Thistle stabs, the Rose pricks, the Sword-grass cuts, the Tulip soothes, and the Ragged Robin calls in the Deadly Nightshade who bottles up his pride and allows himself to be made use of.

But the Shamrock stands aside, he sees everything—through everything—and round everything, for he has three faces, and grew up in the Island of Green, and has lived for a very long time. Were it not for the Poppy, however, presiding, as she does, over the healers and their magic, the garden containing these particular plants would by no means thrive. For she is able to take the stab from the Thistle, the prick from the Rose, the cut from the Sword-grass, and the deadliness from the Night-shade. And so the mortals bless her—and the plants bless her too ; for it is to her that they owe their means of living. For who would go into the garden and be cut, scratched, or stabbed without her ?

Now the Thistle was clever—oh ! he was very clever ! He had a head on him, and no mistake ! He had more magic in him than any of the healers, and so he was the most thought of, and the most talked of among the mortals. He had found a way to set their breathings right when they had gone wrong, which they were always doing, because mortals are so very mortal ! And for that they had crowned him. The healers were very proud of their brother, and had come to make their obeisance to him and to praise him.

And, at the same time, there came into the garden a mortal —beautiful, tender, and rare. She was come to beseech the Thistle to save her mate, whose breathing had gone very wrong indeed. Her mate, you must know, was not as other mortals— he was a chosen one ; the gods had bestowed upon him one of their rarest gifts—the gift of making wonder pictures ; and the wonder that he made passed understanding ; but his breathing had gone very wrong indeed, and only the Thistle could save him. How was she to get at the Thistle though ?—for at his gate stood the formidable old Hoe, with orders to let nobody pass, at least nobody who wanted healing, for his time was all taken up.

But, as I have said, the mortal was beautiful, tender, and rare ; and the formidable old Hoe fell under his spell and was beguiled into disobeying her master's orders and beseeching him to see her.

The Thistle was angry—he could heal no more. How dare she come and ask him ! But, as I have said, the Hoe was bewitched, and allowed the Beautiful One to wait ; and she waited and waited and waited. At last, out of patience, the old Hoe determined to go and rout out the healers who were in her master's presence, and off she went to do it. She didn't care, not she, why should she ? "Come on now, Sir Shamrock," said she, giving him a dig, "and you, Mr Sword-grass, and you, too, Rosie, me darlin'," said she, actually daring to dig the sumptuous, peerless, flawless Rose, Healer-in-Chief to their Majesties, unceremoniously in the ribs, and rake him out with the others—the Ragged Robin and the Tulip included ! They were all the same to her, they were, and why not ?

"And now, Thistle, me darlin'," said she, turning to her master, "I'll be bringing the Beautiful One to ye, for she'll fill yer eyes and yer heart and put ye in a good humour for the day."

And in that moment in walked the mortal, beautiful, tender, and rare. The Thistle gazed at her spellbound, and knew in that moment that he wanted her for his own.

"Healer," she faltered.

"Listen to me," said the Thistle, regaining his self-control and making himself appear hard and sharp. (That was not difficult.) "I cannot help you, my time is taken up. I must therefore wish you good morning."

"Healer," she pleaded insistently, "my mate is no ordinary mortal, he is gifted of the gods, and makes pictures, and the wonder of them passeth understanding. You will understand, I know, for you have beautiful ones of your own," said she, gazing round his garden. (That flattered him.) "Look, I will show you one of his." And the Thistle found himself gazing on a picture of the Beautiful One herself, and was overcome with the wonder of it. He thought quickly.

"Is your mate well enough to come to a feast?" he asked.

"Yes, yes," said the Beautiful One eagerly, hope springing up in her heart.

"Very well, then," continued the Thistle. "I am giving a feast to my brother healers. You and your mate shall come to it, as I intend to leave it to my brothers to decide whether I am to save your mate or not. They are to be his judges, and you must promise to abide by their decision. Will you do this?" he asked sternly.

" I will," said she.

And so it was arranged. The feast was prepared ; the healers were gathered together ; and the Beautiful One was there with her mortal mate ; and everything in the garden was lovely—at least, everyone thought so, except the Shamrock, for he has three faces, and sees everything, through everything, and round everything, and he saw the cloven hoof of her mortal mate which—as yet—no other eyes had seen.

The feast was over. It had been a sumptuous one, and everyone had been happy. The Beautiful One and her gifted mate had made themselves beloved by all. And now they were departing to leave the healers to discuss among themselves whether the Thistle was to save the Gifted One or not.

The Beautiful One was full of anxiety. "What do you think of my mate?" she enquired of the healers, timidly ; "or ought I not to ask you?"

The healers were at her feet in a moment. They all wanted to save him.

"He is brilliant," said the Sword-grass. "Leave him to me, I'll cut him up and make him whole for you."

"No, no," said the Rose, "leave him to me. He's charming ; I will prick him and put new life into him."

"I think Deadly Nightshade or green would be good for

him," said the Ragged Robin gently. But the Shamrock and the Tulip were silent, each for reasons of his own.

And the Thistle knew that he alone could save him, and the Beautiful One knew it too. She looked at him, waiting for him to speak.

"He is gifted of the gods, and must and shall be saved," said the Thistle at last.

"Oh, you have made me happy," said she, with tears in her eyes; "how can I ever repay you?" Her faith in him knew no bounds. "And now we will go."

And they took their departure and were soon out of sight.

Now the Ragged Robin, who had been absent for a time, returned. Looking hastily round, he asked anxiously where the mortals were.

"They have gone," said the Thistle.

"Gone?" repeated the Ragged Robin in distress. "I must go after them." And away he raced as fast as his legs would carry him. But alas! he could not catch them, and back he came again.

"What has happened?" the others asked.

The poor Ragged Robin was too embarrassed to tell them— he hated being a Ragged Robin—how degrading it was!

"You must tell us," said the healers, whose suspicions were beginning to be aroused.

"Is it anything to do with the Gifted One?" demanded the Thistle, sternly.

"It is, oh! it is," confessed the poor Ragged Robin. "I lent him some of my silver—I only had just enough to get back into the woods with—and he's gone without returning it to me. What am I to do? How can I get back?"

"You lent him silver?" boomed the Rose. "Why, I lent him gold—ten pieces of gold."

"And I, twenty pieces," cut in the Sword-grass.

The Thistle was troubled. "Did he get anything out of you, Tulip?"

"No," said the Tulip, "I do not lend money without the certainty of getting it back, and I didn't think there was any certainty about him."

The other healers were uncomfortable at that. They were of a different breed, you see. But as it turned out, the Tulip was right. The Shamrock could have warned the others—that is, if you can warn others. He had seen the cloven hoof from the beginning. Now the others had found it out for themselves.

"The cloven hoof, the cloven hoof," they cried in disgust. "He isn't a true mortal, then, he's half a beast! A satyr! A satyr! *Ugh*!"

At that moment a little ewe lamb came trotting up. "Where is that He-mortal?" she bleated. "Where is my mate?"

"Your mate?" cried the healers in astonishment and dismay.

"Yes, he is my mate; I can prove it to you," she cried.

" You needn't," said the Shamrock, grimly ; " we can believe anything."

" You see," said he, turning to the healers, " he's more than half a beast—he's an out-and-out beast."

" Come, I say, Shamrock, aren't you a bit hard on him ? " said the benevolent Ragged Robin.

" He's very young, you know, and his mate is very charming," boomed the Rose.

" It's getting positively intriguing," cut in the Sword-grass, flippantly.

The cloven hoof seemed to matter very little to them after all.

" Do you realise," interrupted the Thistle, sharply, " that I have promised to save that creature's life ? "

" Can you save it ? " asked the Ragged Robin in astonishment. (He hadn't heard what the Thistle's magic was.)

" Yes," said the Thistle, " I can."

" Well, will you save mine ? " said the Ragged Robin, " for my breathings have gone wrong."

The healers were most concerned over their poor brother, the Thistle and the Shamrock most of all ; and the Shamrock saw to it that the Ragged Robin got home safely with the others.

When they were gone the Shamrock and the Thistle were left alone. " You have got to make a choice, Thistle," said the Shamrock, gravely. " Which will you save, the Ragged Robin or the Satyr—for it seems that you must make your choice between one who Heals and one who Destroys ? "

"It's not so easy as that, Shamrock," said the Thistle, scintillatingly cynical. "The Healer destroys, too. He destroys the look of the garden (the Ragged Robin was no beauty), whereas the Destroyer, as you call him, immortalises it."

"Don't be clever with me, Thistle. What is the garden in comparison with the hearts the Satyr has destroyed?"

"Oh! I'm not sure that it wouldn't be better if everyone behaved as the Satyr does."

"Why don't you, then?" asked the Shamrock, quietly.

"Ah! Shamrock, you have me there; I couldn't."

"No, I thought not," grunted the old Shamrock.

"But now," said the Thistle, "you must listen to me, for I have a confession to make to you. I love the Beautiful One, the Satyr's mate, so that if I decide to kill the beast I shall mate with her myself."

"Don't dare to talk to me about killing the beast in that ruthless way of yours," thundered the Shamrock. "As a member of the noble brotherhood of healers, you can't do that, you know."

"No," said the Thistle, laughing wickedly, "I suppose I can't, but I *can* hand him over to the blooming, booming Rose for *him* to blunder over and kill, can't I?" (Imagine the Rose's feelings if he heard that!)

"The blooming, booming Rose is a very eminent healer," remarked the Shamrock, drily; "no blame could be attached to you for doing that."

The Thistle's mind, however, was not yet made up. He was a strong and upright plant, and he must be very sure that he was justified in handing the Satyr over to the Rose to blunder over. But on one thing he was determined, the Satyr should not get off scot free. He would gather the healers together once more, this time to judge him in real earnest.

He went to the Satyr's home. The beautiful young creature welcomed him with grace and charm. Oh ! he was unbelievably charming and disarming.

"You've come about my breathings, Thistle ; how good of you. But really it's not so much that I lack breath as that I lack gold. I am going to treat you as a friend, you know, and ask you to give me one hundred and fifty gold pieces. You will, won't you ? "

"No, I will not," said the Thistle, sharply.

"Why not ? " asked the Satyr in surprise.

"Because I need them myself."

"Oh, if you wanted them back, you could always get them from my mate by telling her that it would harm me if she didn't give them to you," said the unscrupulous young monster, airily.

The Thistle was speechless. "He'd even rob his mate ! Was there no limit to his baseness ? "

At that moment, in came the other healers. "Sit down, sit down, all of you," said the Satyr, gaily.

"We've not come to sit down, sir," said the Shamrock,

dangerously. "We've come to make you sit up! You robbed the Robin."

"Robbed the Robin," mused the Satyr; "that sounds pretty, but it's sad, because he was a Ragged Robin. Sword-grass, lend me some silver to repay the poor Ragged Robin."

The Sword-grass was staggered. "You took my golden case from me," he replied cuttingly.

"Did I? Well, I've not let the grass grow under my feet, for I have sold it for this little card," said the Satyr, sweetly. "I didn't know it was yours, Sword-grass. Here's the card. You can easily buy it back, you know. Have I done anything else?" said he, sunnily.

"Do you happen to know a little ewe-lamb?" asked the Shamrock, shortly.

"Of course I do—the sweet little thing! I gave her a wonderful time."

"She says she's your mate," said the Sword-grass.

"So does the Beautiful One," replied the Satyr, tauntingly. The healers, one and all, felt savage. Was there no limit to this unspeakable creature, who would sacrifice anything and everything, except himself, to his own ends? And was now trying to rob the Beautiful One of her virtue.

The Thistle's mind was made up.

"I'll not heal this creature," said he in anger and disgust. "Will any of you others? Will you, Rose?"

"I will," replied the Rose, "for I make it my rule to think only of the body. In this case, however, I shall not think of him at all, but of his mate, for she has begged me to save him for her."

He really believed that she had. (Those rose-coloured glasses of his !)

"Well," said the Shamrock, exchanging glances with the Thistle, "as our dear blooming Rose has kindly offered to take charge of you, Satyr, we will wish you good-day."

"One minute," said the Satyr. "While you bunch of wild flowers have been spreading yourselves, I, the out-and-out beast, have been working my magic. Behold ! "

And, sure enough, there was magic indeed ! The healers were enthralled in spite of themselves.

"I'll sell it to the highest bidder," said the Satyr, seizing his chance of getting more gold out of them.

"All right, I'll have it for twelve gold pieces," said the Rose, taking it from him and presenting it to the Shamrock as a gift. "I needn't pay you for it, Satyr, as my charges for healing you will come to much more than that," said the Rose, deliberately.

"You beastly robber," screamed the Satyr, beside himself with rage, now that he wasn't the robber but the robbed !

The healers looked on coolly.

"Oh, then you do think it beastly to rob, after all ! We're so glad. That's all we came for. Good-bye."

I . . . have been working my magic. Behold!

At that moment the Beautiful One came in. The Shamrock rose to greet her, and to wish her good-bye. She looked at him, at the others—she felt something had happened, she felt a change in all of them.

" Shamrock," she faltered, " what is the matter ? You don't think my mate is worse, do you ? "

" No," said the Shamrock, drily. " He's just the same as he was. No worse, but no better."

" And now," said the Rose, coming toward her in his most beautiful and blooming manner, " as I am going to take care of your mate . . . "

" You ! " cried the Beautiful One, gazing anxiously at the Thistle, " I thought . . . "

" Yes," boomed the Rose, in majestic benevolence, " your mate shall have ME ! I will arrange everything. So good-bye for the present." And off he went, leaving her alone with the Thistle.

She looked at the Thistle.

" You have broken your word to me—why ? "

" Don't ask me why, for I can tell you nothing," said the poor Thistle. He was in a terrible dilemma. How could he tell her of the unspeakable baseness of her beloved ?

" Listen to me, please," pleaded the Beautiful One. " Do not judge my mate by ordinary laws ; he is not ordinary, he is above the laws. If he were to do anything really dishonourable, I should take my life . . . But he couldn't, for he is my beloved, my great one, and I have come to you to beseech you to save him and preserve him for me—you can, I know, my faith in you is boundless."

The Thistle's mind was made up. "I can understand what you tell me," he said very gently, "and I will preserve your great one for you."

"Thank you, oh ! thank you," said she, taking his hands and kissing them.

"Wait, wait," said the Thistle, beseechingly. "Hear me out. The only way I can preserve your hero for you is to hand him over to the Rose. Can you believe me when I say that ? "

"If you say so, I believe, for I believe in you."

And then—she was gone. The Thistle groaned, but his soul was at peace, for he felt that he had decided rightly.

And so the Satyr was handed over to the Rose, who blundered over him as the Thistle and the Shamrock knew he would. And the Satyr died.

But the Beautiful One was not unhappy—for his magic lived, and he lived again in her, and was happier without his Satyr body and the cloven feet.

But what of the Thistle ? Who is to say whether he did right or wrong in sacrificing the Satyr's life to save his mate from misery ? Who is to judge ? If he did do right he got no reward ; for when he went to lay his heart at her feet she laughed him to scorn.

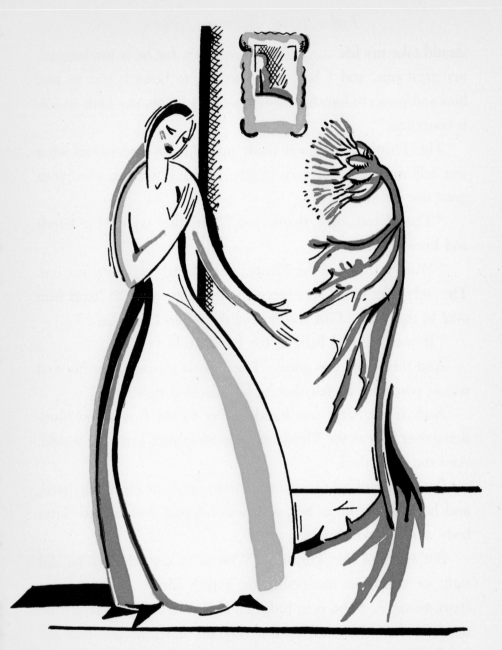

"Can a dried-up old plant like you aspire to me?" cried she in her innocent loveliness

" Can a dried-up old plant like you aspire to me ? " cried she in her innocent loveliness.

Poor Thistle ! Pity his mortification at being thrown away and left—to wither.

CAPTAIN BRASSBOUND'S CONVERSION
or, the Sun shines upon the Just and upon the Unjust

CAPTAIN BRASSBOUND'S CONVERSION

*or, the Sun shines upon the Just and
upon the Unjust*

THERE was once a Genie who caught the Sun, caught
her ! Gave her arms, legs, a voice, and a name. Then
he brought her to earth to show the heathen who live there, how
she works, and what she is really doing, all that way away by
herself ! The Sun was glad the Genie had caught her, because
she was tired of shining only on heathen bodies ; and not even
on all of *them,* for the most civilized heathens make blinds and
clothes and roofs and hats to keep her off !—though they are
beginning to know better. Well, heathens survive somehow,
and the Sun had never given up hope. Then, one day that
clever Genie caught her and gave her the chance that she had
waited for—the chance of shining into heathen hearts instead—
for she knew *they* would never resist her. She was right, they
never did, as you will see.

Now what could have put the idea of catching the Sun into
the Genie's mind ? Heathens call each other mad for crying for
the Moon, let alone for catching the Sun ! I'll tell you. He
knew a heathen infinitely less heathen and infinitely more sun-

like than any of the inhabitants of the earth, and he wanted to immortalize her, and all he had to do it with was a pen ! So he did it with his pen by embodying her in his book and her name was

Now in the Genie's book the Sun was an important person. Her uncle was a head of big ships and her in-law brother was a head in law, and she herself was a celebrated traveller. She had travelled nearly the whole world over ; and by herself, which was unusual, as she was a She. Being her own sunny self, she was irresistible and found no doors closed to her, and no hearts either ! In this story, however, she had an encumbrance travelling with her ; she had her in-law brother the Moon—the exact opposite to herself—for where she brought sunshine, he brought only moonshine ; where she was warm and attracting, he was cold and forbidding—and he made people mad, too ! And so he brought trouble ; and the Sun had to use every bit of her power to get everybody out of it, as you will see.

Why was the Sun travelling with the Moon ? You may well ask. There was a reason. There is always a reason, and the reason was the Law—though I do not mean the heathen law. So that everything that takes place in this story must take place exactly as it does, or the Law would not be fulfilled, as it was and always must be fulfilled. The reason was, that there was a heart in darkness in the desert, a heart of gold ; and the Sun was ordained to liberate it, to give it light, to melt it—for that dark, saturnine hating was—brass-bound ! And brass is alloy, not true metal, and was corrupting the heart of gold within. And so, according to plan, the Sun and the Moon found themselves, at the beginning of our story, knocking at the gate of the Southern Cross, whose mission it was to preach the gospel to the brown coloured heathen who dwell in the desert. (I don't think he succeeded, though ; for the brown heathen thought they had a better gospel of their own, which is the way we all think.)

Now when the Law starts fulfilling itself, we heathen call it coincidence, and the coincidence in this case was, that the Moon and the Southern Cross had met before, the Moon's brother and the Southern Cross had been friends in times gone by. So the Moon talked of his brother and told the Southern Cross how his brother had now passed away and how he had mated and gained lands and thrived. He did not tell him, however, how he had seized those lands from his brother's mate and had driven her into madness ; nor did he tell him how the lands had turned out after all to be valueless ! Neither could he tell him of his brother's son who now lived only to avenge his mother's wrong ; for that he did not know.

When they had talked their fill, they turned their eyes toward the desert and gazed upon its beauty ; and the Sun found herself desiring to go into the heart of it alone. The Southern Cross, however, warned her of the danger that lurked therein ; how that the planet Mars and his hordes of fighting chiefs infested the desert, making it full of danger. But the Sun had heard that sort of talk before and knew better ! She knew that nothing was dangerous to her ; she knew that all she had to do was to be herself, and all would open their hearts to her. How happy that clever Genie had made her !

But the Sun was not to be permitted to roam through the desert by herself this time. The Moon insisted on her having an escort, and the escort she was destined to have, turned out to be no other than the planet Saturn, that dark, brooding, avenging, brass-bound soul that dwelt in the desert alone. And he was sent for, and he came into their presence. No sooner did the Southern Cross set eyes on him than he was spellbound, for lo ! he was the living image of his old friend the Moon's brother—no wonder—for he was his son !

Saturn turned his eyes upon the Moon and his look became blacker and more saturnine than ever ; for before him stood he, who had driven his mother into madness, he who had seized their lands. The moment he had been waiting for was come at last ! The Moon was delivered into his hands ! At least, so thought Saturn in his ignorance. He did not know that the Sun had come all that way to deliver him out of darkness, to show him the Law, to get at the heart of him. For the Law tells us that we have no need to take upon ourselves our own vengeance, it will take our burdens upon itself and avenge our wrongs for us—in its own time and in its own way.

"We have sent for you, Saturn," the Moon was saying, "to escort us into the desert."

"Yes, Saturn, we'd rather have you than anyone," beamed the Sun, "your face is so beautiful and good."

Saturn turned his inscrutable eyes upon her for one half moment ; and in that moment a ray of light found its way in ; so that 'something in him' made him warn the Moon of the danger that lurked in the desert for him. "The desert is no place for him who has done injury to another, O Moon ! " said Saturn, darkly. "I warn you not to come."

"I am not afraid," answered the Moon, coldly, "for I have done no one injury in all my life."

Now, strangely enough, that was true—at least the Moon believed it to be true ! Although he had done such grievous wrong to Saturn's mother, he was unaware of it ; he felt no sin of it upon his heart ; for his heart was cold, unawakened, proof even against the Sun. Its time was not yet—the Law was not concerning itself with it, but with the warm, aching, hating heart of Saturn. And it was decreed that they should all go into the desert together so as to give the Sun her chance of getting at the heart of Saturn. And she was to get nearer to it than either she or he dreamed of.

As the Moon refused to take the warning Saturn had so generously offered him, his blood was on his own head ! No sooner did they approach the desert than the Moon began to realize that something was wrong, for celestial bodies expect all other bodies to keep their distance. The nearer they got to the desert, however, the nearer Saturn's band of satellites seemed to be getting to him ; they seemed to be surrounding him in a very sinister manner. At last, one of them jostled him, it was unbelievable—because of all bodies the Moon is the most cold and the most distant.

" Saturn," said the Moon, sharply, " I command you to see that your satellites do not encroach upon me ; that they show the deference due to me as one of the heads of the greatest kingdom of my world."

Saturn looked at him menacingly.

" I do not see you in that light at all ; all I see is a cold, cruel murderer and thief."

The Sun looked up, startled.

" You are in my power now," continued Saturn, sternly, " to do with as I please."

" Do I understand, then, that you are a brigand, and have brought me here to destroy me ? " demanded the Moon, freezingly.

And she was to get nearer . . . than either she or he dreamed of

" I warned you not to come, did I not ? If I am a brigand, then you are the uncle of one ! "

" Uncle of one ! " cried the Sun and Moon in astonishment. " What do you mean ? "

" Who are you ? What are you ? " cried the Moon, hoarsely.

" I am your brother's son, behold me ! "

At these words the Moon's face darkened ominously.

" You mean to say, then, that that creature was your mother ! "

Imagine the effect of these words on any mother's son ! Saturn leapt at the Moon, to strangle him—to choke the words in his throat. But the Sun, turning her beautiful radiance upon Saturn, begged of him to spare his uncle.

" He is old and cold, Saturn," she pleaded, " spare him."

" Did he spare my mother when she was old and alone ? "

" She was mad, a positive thunderbolt ; I could do nothing with her nor for her," said the Moon, icily.

" Who was it drove her mad ? " cried Saturn, beside himself with passion. " You, you beastly, hypocritical, ice-bound creature ; wrapping yourself up in the robes of law and justice. You shall see, now that you are old and alone like my mother, what all that hypocrisy and moonshine, heathen law, will do for you. I have sent for the planet Mars ; he administers the law in these parts ; and you shall get a taste of what you meted out to my mother."

The Moon was far more enraged by the insult to the dignity of the law than he was afraid for his own safety. His only passion was for his calling ; and now it had been insulted, belittled, dragged in the dust—by a brigand ! Saturn had indeed drawn blood from a stone ! The Moon controlled his fury—he at least commanded respect for that—and said icily :

" I trust I shall conduct myself as befits a just and upright representative of the law ; and as for your lands that you accuse me of stealing," he continued grandiosely, " they are yours for the asking ; I was unaware of your existence until this moment. Take your lands ; I have no wish to rob you of your inheritance —I do not want them."

At this the Sun looked up quaintly.

" No, I don't suppose you do, Moon, now that you've found out they are valueless."

The Moon was extremely annoyed that the Sun should choose such a moment to let the truth slip out. Saturn gazed at him speechless, and his clean, strong, decent heart sickened.

" *Faugh,* you trickster ! Take him away. He pollutes the very air we breathe."

And Saturn's satellites surrounded, pushed, shoved, jostled the Moon and sent him rolling—the indignity of it was quite terrible to see !

Saturn and the Sun were left alone, he raging and fuming ; she shining serenely ! An unequal situation—and no mistake !

for he could not rage and fume as long as she could smile serenely—and she was well aware of it !

"Do you know," said she, mischievously, " that you and your uncle are very much alike ? "

Saturn stared at her in fury.

"You dare to liken me to that cold, cruel, ice-bound thing ? " he exclaimed savagely.

"Yes, I do, for you both believe in the same things—revenge, punishment, cruelty ; all those cold, dead unrealities, don't you, Brassbound ? " she said softly.

"Why do you call me 'Brassbound' ? Saturn is my name. Can't you realize the danger you are in ? "

"All you creatures talk of danger ; I can't see danger in anything."

"Then you must be mad—or a fool ! "

"I am not a bit mad, Saturn ; so I suppose I must be a fool ; for all I can do is to shine and shine—upon the just and upon the unjust. I suppose you *would* call that foolish, wouldn't you ? It isn't even fair, is it—is it ? " she repeated softly.

Saturn was speechless, powerless ; he could not answer her one way or the other ; she was getting at him, that was the truth of the matter.

"Why did you come here ? " he groaned. "My trap was not laid for you but for him. Why have you come ? "

"To help you, Brassbound," she said softly.

" No one can help me or change me," he answered curtly.

" Oh, I can't believe you are as obstinate as all that."

Now no one can bear to be called obstinate !

" Obstinate ! " said Saturn, crossly.

" Oh, I suppose I ought to have said resolute, powerful, strong, silent man, eh, Brassbound ? "

" Now you are laughing at me," he cried in despair. " Curse you, curse you, you have belittled me ; belittled my reason for existence, my vengeance for my mother ; everything I have been, and everything I have done, and everything is now turned into ashes."

" Ah, no, no, Brassbound. I believe in you, in the real you, in the heart of gold within you. No one could belittle that, you know. I am only getting at the dross that surrounds you."

He looked intently at her. She had touched his heart, and she knew it !

At that moment Saturn's satellites rushed in to warn him that one of Mars' chiefs was racing toward them over the desert like a whirlwind.

" Is the Moon in danger ? " asked the Sun.

" In great danger," answered Saturn, " for I have given my word to the Chief, that the Moon shall be handed over to him to do with as he pleases. That was to be my revenge. What am I to do now ? If I do not keep my word to the Chief there will be trouble for all of us."

And at that moment in ran another with the news that Mars

himself was on his way toward them and that the whole desert was alive with hordes of fighting heathen.

" We are saved ! " said Saturn, " for if any harm comes to the Moon through the Chief, it will be Mars himself who will have to answer to the powers that be ; so that Mars will see that the Chief doesn't harm the Moon, and if we can only gain time and keep him parleying till Mars arrives, all will be well. Stand by, everyone, to receive the Chief."

The heathen Chief and his brown coloured followers arrived upon the scene.

" Welcome, Saturn. I have come to claim the infidel. Which is he of all these heathen ? " The brown heathen despised the white ones as much as the white despised the brown —doesn't that seem funny to us ?

" Here is the Moon, O Chief," said Saturn, presenting the Moon, who had been sent for.

The Chief's face fell, the Moon looked so awfully forbidding ! !

He thought quickly. " I have been informed, O Saturn, that the Sun is with you. Where is she ? "

" Here, Chief, here I am, and pleased to meet you," said the Sun, coming out at that moment and beaming upon him.

The Chief gazed upon her spellbound ; and, with true Eastern wisdom, immediately decided that he would keep the Sun himself, and give the Moon back to Saturn ! Who could blame him ?

"No! no!" cried Saturn and the Moon in horror at the thought of a brown He-chief taking a white She, to do with as he pleased—it was unthinkable, wasn't it, now?

But the Sun, to everyone's astonishment, said, "I will go with the Chief."

"You can't; you don't know what you are doing," said Saturn, entreatingly.

"You don't suppose he'll treat you as a white heathen would, do you?" said the Moon, aghast.

"No, he won't treat me like a heathen at all!" said the Sun, smiling. "Look at his beautiful, noble face!"

At that moment in came Mars, towering with rage.

"Thou dog," said he, turning savagely to his Chief; "what art thou doing, meddling with the white heathen. The fault is Saturn's, that I know; he has brought trouble upon us all. Neptune and the whole seafaring heathen are getting ready to wash us away, if any harm should come to the Sun or to the Moon. I take thee prisoner, Saturn, thou and thy band of satellites," and they were seized and bound without further ado.

The Moon looked on coldly.

"It's your turn now," said he to Saturn, contemptuously.

The Sun looked on, too, her thoughts already fixed on Neptune and how she must find a way to induce him to free Saturn.

Mars then gave orders; and they all proceeded on their way back.

Now, Neptune was to try the prisoner Saturn at the house of

the Southern Cross. The Sun had made her plans for saving him, but she needed the Southern Cross to help her carry them out, and she went there to tell him.

"You expect me to help that black-hearted brigand," said the Southern Cross, aghast, "after what he has done or tried to do to the Moon?"

"You can't go by what the Moon says, he's a very one-sided fellow ; he's in the law, you know, and paid to be that way," said she, sunnily. "Now, if it had been his mission to preach the gospel, as it is yours, Southern Cross, he wouldn't be one-sided, would he?—for every word he said would be gospel!"

These words had a wonderful effect on the Southern Cross (they were meant to), but he wasn't quite convinced.

"Mars himself told me that Saturn was a well-known brigand," said he.

"Well now, if Saturn really is a brigand, we must try and convert him, for it will never do for the Moon to have a brigand for a nephew, will it now?"

"The Moon's nephew! What do you mean?" said the Southern Cross in amazement.

"Oh, didn't the Moon tell you they were related? That's why they quarrelled, you know. They are uncle and nephew. Saturn is the son of your old friend. It was very wrong of the Moon not to tell you at once. Now you see for yourself what a one-sided fellow he is!"

The Southern Cross was thoroughly convinced now and willing to do everything he could to help his old friend's son.

"I'll go to the prison and see what I can do for him," said the Southern Cross, quite overcome.

"How good you are! Now let us put our heads together and see how we can best help him. It's his appearance, isn't it? —so saturnine! It will give Neptune quite a wrong impression of him, won't it? Now I have some things here, suitable for Saturn; take them with you, and tell him from me to put them on—he will, I know—and tell him to polish his face up, too!" And she bustled the Southern Cross out as quickly as she could, for she saw the Moon approaching and didn't want him to know what she was up to.

"Oh, Moon, I'm so sorry for you," said she, sympathetically.

The Moon looked at her in astonishment.

"About your nephew, I mean. Neptune might convict him! He probably will, and then we shall have a convict for a relation!"

"As a representative of the law I cannot allow my personal feeling to come between a malefactor and his punishment," said the Moon, austerely.

"Well, then, a representative of the law shouldn't have relations; for Saturn may tell Neptune all about his mother; how you drove her mad and seized her lands; and all the world will know, and think you a wicked, clever lawyer who robbed a poor, defenceless mother! And they'll think Saturn was quite justified in handing you over to the brown heathen Chief in revenge."

The Moon was alarmed, in spite of himself.

"What do you suggest can be done ? " said he, quickly.

"I'll tell you what to do," said the Sun, cheerfully. "Leave me to tell Neptune the whole story myself."

"But can I trust you to speak the truth, the whole truth, and nothing but the truth ? " asked the Moon, suspiciously. (It was his job to be suspicious, poor fellow.)

"Implicitly ! " beamed the Sun, delighted with her success !

At that moment Neptune appeared, ready to conduct the trial.

"How do you do, Neptune ? How handsome and manly all you sea creatures are," beamed the Sun. She was incorrigible !

"Really," said the Moon, reprovingly, "please remember that this represents a Court of Justice and must be conducted as such."

"Oh, Neptune understands me, I am sure. Sea creatures like us She-creatures to be ourselves; they see so little of us, you know ; that's why they go melancholy mad from time to time and ram each other's ships and get into all sorts of trouble."

The Moon was terribly shocked. He was part of a world where they think these things but do not express them !

But Neptune smiled and smiled, and the Sun smiled back at him !

" And now, Neptune, if you'll excuse me, I'll go and see what they are doing with the prisoner," and out she went !

Neptune couldn't say a word, for she'd taken his breath away, and everybody else's too !

Quite shortly the Sun returned with Saturn, polished up and looking as beautiful as Apollo, and, with his brassy brigandry gone, as respectable as the Moon himself !

Neptune was dumbfounded. This was a very different creature from what he'd been led to expect. The Moon was taken aback too, and secretly wondered what devilment the Sun was up to.

" And, Neptune, now that you have seen the prisoner, let me explain the whole cause of the trouble to you, and why these two, Saturn and the Moon, quarrelled."

" Quarrelled ? " said Neptune. " I have been officially informed that Saturn deliberately plotted to hand the Moon over to the Chief of the brown coloured heathen."

" He didn't do so, Neptune ; he only threatened to do so, because the Moon said dreadful things about his mother. You couldn't expect Saturn to stand that, could you ? "

" No, certainly not," said Neptune. " Proceed."

" Well, when they found out that they were related——"

" Related ! ! ! "

" Yes, that's why they quarrelled ! They are nephew and uncle. See how alike they are (and how furious they were) ; now you understand, don't you, Neptune ? "

Neptune could see quite well what she was after, and he chivalrously decided to let her have her way! (They do that sort of thing where he came from.)

"Say no more, Sun-lady, there's no more to be said. Family quarrels! I understand perfectly. The case is dismissed. The nephew is free; and the uncle," turning to the Moon, "and you, too, charming Sun-lady, will, I hope, do me the honour to lunch with me on my ship."

And so the clouds were dispersed and the Sun shone, and everybody was as happy as the day.

Everybody, that is, save Saturn; with him it was quite otherwise. He had been living in the clouds; and now that they were dispersed he had nowhere to go, nothing to do! His vengeance, the reason for his very existence—had been taken from him. The Sun had shown it up in its true colours, had made it look ridiculous. Nothing can survive that! He had thought the Moon so wicked. Was he as wicked as he had thought? Was he any wickeder than he was himself? And his mother—what of her? His mother that he had thought so good, was she as good as he thought—or wished to think? He gazed upon her picture that he had gazed upon so many, many times; now it looked different; for, with his heart full of sunshine, with the clouds banished for ever, he was able for the first time to see his mother's face as it really was; and what he saw in it hurt him—disillusioned him. The Sun was right in everything—her radiance shone above everything. At that moment in she came ! Saturn looked at her.

"Listen to me," said he, "when you first came across me I was a being with a definite course to run. I stood alone, strong in my own beliefs and my own actions. You have shattered my beliefs, destroyed my strength, shipwrecked me, and, worst of all, you have given me nothing to take the place of the ashes you have left. What is to become of me, what am I to do ? "

"Do what you want to do, it is the only thing to do, Brassbound," she said.

"You have even taken that power from me, for you've shown me, that, left to myself, I do wrong. I used to think myself a leader—Saturn, the Black one, and his satellites ! *Bah !* it is I who need a leader to tell me what to do," said he, looking at her, "and that leader must be you. I need you. Will you mate with me ? "

The Sun was taken aback.

"Do you wish to mate with me, Saturn ? "

"I wish to take service under you, and the only way I can do that is by mating with you," cried Saturn, coming toward her.

"But I am not in love with you."

"Are you in love with anyone else ? "

"No ! For how could I be the power that I am if I gave myself into the power of another ? That's my secret," she said deliberately, looking into his eyes.

"You have made yourself mine now by telling me your secret," said he, masterfully. He was a born master, could rule and dominate whether he would or no. That power he was now unconsciously using on her. She felt it, felt herself succumbing to him.

"You are dangerous, Saturn," she said faintly. "I don't want to give myself to you."

He stretched out his arms to her.

"No! no!" she murmured, her strength leaving her.

"You must," said he, taking her to him.

At that moment the signal for his return resounded through the desert.

"What is that?" she whispered.

Saturn gazed at the radiant creature that lay in his arms. "Your release," said he. "Your surrender to me has made me; your secret is now my secret—your power, my power!"

"Brassbound!"

"No longer Brassbound," said he in ecstasy. "Free! Free to love you where before I was bound to love you—for then I needed you; I hadn't strength to steer my course without you; but your radiance has opened my eyes; your heart has awakened my heart, you have made me myself, you have made me yours— made me free. Farewell."

"Whew! what an attractive creature, what a narrow escape!" said the Sun, as she gazed after the Heart-of-Gold speeding his way, shining in his own light—in darkness no longer.

And the Law was fulfilled, as it always must be fulfilled. For there is more joy in the heavens over one sinner that repenteth—

THE DEVIL'S DISCIPLE
or, Born in Captivity

THE DEVIL'S DISCIPLE

or, Born in Captivity

TO rear a creature in captivity is to stunt it—to take it out of the true, so that it is maimed, does not grow in its own way, nor know its own nature, nor fulfil itself. But the nature is there, nevertheless, awaiting the chance that must come to it sooner or later—later or sooner.

Now the two animals in this story were born in the ordinary way, behind the bars of one of these civilized Zoological Gardens.

One of the animals was fortunate, for his cage was large, almost large enough for him to roam about in as he would. So that he grew up easy, docile, gentle ; and his keepers labelled him 'Lamb,' his neighbours took him for a lamb, he believed himself to be one, and, indeed, became one, for he took on lamb's clothing, and became a disciple of the Lamb of God, and his name was Antony.

The other animal was unfortunate ; he was born in a small, mean, narrow cage, his keepers fought with him and with each other all day long in envy, hatred, and malice (bars against happiness, and no mistake), and the iron entered into his soul, for he was young, defenceless, and tender.

And because he was defenceless and tender his keepers teased and taunted him, which warped and wounded him, so that he grew up the antithesis of a lamb ; he became vicious and snarling, biting and cruel ; his keepers then labelled him ' Jackal ' (dangerous, keep off !), his neighbours treated him as a jackal, and he (almost) believed himself to be a jackal. So that when he grew strong enough, he bit through the narrow bars that bound him, and escaped and became a pariah, and his name was Dick, and he had the devil in him.

Now you must know, first of all, that a Little Zoo over the Seas owned the great big enormous Zoo that Antony and Devil Dick were born in. But the animals in the big Zoo were beginning to rebel ; they wanted to manage their own affairs and own their own Zoo, so they had begun to plot.

The Little Zoo, however, heard of their plottings, and determined to subdue the rebellious creatures by seizing the ringleaders of every section and hanging them up by their necks and killing them—quite a civilized thing to do !

In fact, they had already started and had hanged one animal from the Jackal section. Devil Dick had been to look on at the hanging, so had one of Dick's keepers. They didn't go together, not they, for Devil Dick was a pariah. And—as it happened— so was the Jackal they had hanged ; for he belonged to Dick's own family and was Dick's uncle and his keeper's brother.

Now the Little Zoo's army had made a mistake—they hadn't meant to hang a pariah jackal at all—there was no example in

The two animals . . . were born . . . behind the bars of one of
these . . . Zoological Gardens

that. They had wanted a lamb for the slaughter ; to make an example of ; to show the rebels how dangerous it was to plot against them, and so they determined that when they got to the next section they would pick a real good lamb and hang him up as a warning to all rebellious animals.

Devil Dick had got wind of their intentions, and knew that the lamb they meant to seize was Antony.

Now Dick had not been near his own section since the days when he had bitten his way through those narrow bars that bound him. But now he must return, for his keeper had died at the sight of his brother hanging (a truly awful spectacle), and Dick, being the eldest born, was now the owner of the family cage and he must go and claim it.

So the outcast, the pariah, went back into the fold. He gazed round him. There was his other keeper taunting, teasing, narrow—as of old. There were his uncles—mean, smug, sanctimonious as of old. And there was Antony and Antony's mate.

He eyed them all scornfully, they were so virtuous (he was so vicious !). The more he eyed them the more he despised them, and the more biting and cruel he became, and the angrier and angrier they became ; all except Antony. For the more Dick tried to bite and tear at Antony, the more gentle Antony became ; not only because of his good heart, but because of his good sense—and the Jackal could not but feel that Antony had got the better of him.

But he did not feel that way toward his uncles or his keeper.

So he made himself master in his own cage and frightened them all out with his devilry, and they were glad to get away from him ; even Antony, on account of his mate, and Dick was left alone triumphant.

Now Antony believed that the Little Zoo army was on its way to their section to hang Dick, and being the good creature that he was, he determined to try and save him. So he went the next day in search of him—but Dick's cage was empty. Leaving signals that would tell the ' Jackal ' that he wanted to see him, Antony went home to his own cage and told his mate about it. But his mate was afraid ; she felt that trouble was coming to them, and begged Antony to have nothing to do with Dick, for he was a devil. And at that moment Dick stood in the doorway.

" Come in, ' Jackal,' " said the ' Lamb,' hospitably, " I want to talk to you."

The ' Jackal's ' lip curled ; he loved to taunt as he had been taunted.

" You're hospitable to me now that I am no longer a pariah and have a cage of my own, aren't you ? " said he, unworthily.

Antony's mate showed her teeth in anger.

" If you thought as little of me as that, ' Jackal,' " said Antony, gently, " you would not have come to my cage, would you ? Come in and eat with us."

Dick looked at him. looked him through and through.

"I don't think I will come into your cage, Antony, or eat with you," he said quietly.

"What's your reason?" asked the 'Lamb,' quite simply.

"There's something in you that I respect, therefore I'd rather keep you as an enemy, if you don't mind."

That was a strange thing to say, but strange things are said. Maybe something in the 'Jackal,' stranger than himself, made him say it; something that knew the heart within him better than he knew it himself; that told him that his heart could love and suffer and sacrifice. Ah—was that the danger he instinctively feared—sacrifice! Could it be possible that he was not a jackal at all—but a lamb—a lamb capable of giving its life for another?

Antony succeeded at last in coaxing the 'Jackal' into his cage to eat and to talk with them; and the 'Jackal's' rebellious heart was soothed.

And then the 'Jackal's' brother came in—a quaint guinea-pig looking creature, very different from his brother. Seeing his brother, the 'Jackal,' in the 'Lamb's' cage he was surprised.

"Our keeper is dying," said he, laconically.

"She doesn't want to see me, though, I'll be bound," said Devil Dick in his most biting manner. (He hated his keeper as much as she hated him.)

"No, she doesn't. She wants the 'Lamb' to give her his blessing."

"I'll come willingly," said Antony, and turning to his mate he bade her keep the 'Jackal' till he returned.

"Must I?" she faltered. She was mortally afraid of the 'Jackal,' for some reason or another best known to herself.

"You must," said the 'Lamb,' tenderly but firmly, for the 'Lamb' knew (or thought he knew) of the 'Jackal's' danger and wanted to save him if possible.

When he was gone his mate and the 'Jackal' sat together in the 'Lamb's' happy, comfortable cage. And the 'Jackal' felt at peace for the first time in his life. The only cage he had ever known had been a prison; here was one that was a nest.

But his peace was short-lived, for to their horror they heard a tramping outside of footpads, and the sound stopped at the cage door. They gazed at each other—could it be . . . ? The next moment some of the Little Zoo army entered the cage. Seeing the 'Jackal' sitting there with Antony's mate they naturally took him for Antony.

"I arrest you, Antony, the Lamb, as a rebel, in the name of the King of the Little Zoo," said the Chief, entering the cage and laying his hands on Dick.

Then it was that the true nature of the 'Jackal' was revealed!

He was not a jackal, but a lamb—willing to give his life for another; willing to allow the soldiers to take him, and hang him, believing him to be Antony. And Antony's mate looked

A full-blooded Lion—at your service

on in horror and dismay, unable to move, unable to speak, unable to save him !

"Do not tell him," Dick whispered, quickly and quietly ; "it will do no good, he cannot save me ; they would hang him just the same and not spare me ; let him save himself. And now, kiss me good-bye, or the soldiers will not believe that I am your mate."

And she kissed him ! And he was gone—to his death. She sank to the ground as one dead—for in that kiss she had known both heaven and hell.

Antony returned to find his cage in darkness. What had happened ? Where was his mate ? Why had he been so foolish as to leave her alone with a jackal ? She had been right, after all ! And then he caught sight of her lying on the floor, motionless. He picked her up, she opened her eyes, but she could not speak. Her tongue was tied. She could tell him nothing, for she knew or thought she knew that if she told him that Dick had been taken to be hanged he would go to help him and so to his own death ; and she couldn't tell him they had come for himself, for Dick had told her not to.

What was she to do ? The torment was too great—the memory of the 'Jackal's' lamb-like sacrifice—the beauty and nobility of the creature as he made it, wrung her heart in anguish—and she was powerless to save him ; she must try to think only of her mate and not of him.

"*Baa, baa,*" bleated a little ewe lamb outside the door. "Di-ick, Di-ick, where is he?"

And then Antony guessed that they had taken Dick.

"I must go to him," said Antony, quickly.

"No, no, he said you must not," cried his mate in anguish. "Why?"

"I can't tell you, I can't tell you," said she, weeping bitterly.

Antony was puzzled. But bit by bit he forced the truth from her. When she could withhold it no longer, she told him everything.

"If you go to Dick you go to your death, for it was for you that the soldiers came."

At these words the true nature of the 'Lamb' revealed itself. He wasn't a lamb at all, he was a raging, roaring lion; a creature not for sacrifice, but to fight to the death. His blood was up, answering the call of battle. He knew what to do, there was no time to be lost. His mate looked on in horror as he, with one bounding leap, was out of the cage, out of sight, gone— without a word of farewell.

So, he was running away; leaving Dick to die; saving his own skin. How she despised him!—she shuddered. She would be his mate no longer.

How little we know of our best beloved. How little we know even of ourselves.

And what of Dick?

He was caged now, in real earnest. But because he had had

strength to bite through the bars that bound his soul the bars that now bound his body left him undaunted ; so that he won the admiration of his captors ; especially that of the great Big Bug Burgoyne, who was to try him.

Dick was brought as a prisoner into the court, followed by Antony's mate, who now refused to be parted from him.

"What is your name, sir ? " demanded one of the Chiefs.

Dick looked at him cynically. "You ought to know that, since you are hanging me," was his taunting reply.

"I warn you to be careful. What do you expect me to think of you if you answer me that way ? "

"I never expect a soldier to think," answered the 'Jackal' contemptuously.

Big Bug Burgoyne was so tickled at that, that he would willingly have freed the 'Jackal' on the spot.

"Will you tell us your name, then," said Burgoyne, politely, "as a matter of form ? "

"Well, then, as a matter of form," said the 'Jackal,' with equal politeness, "my name is Antony."

"Don't believe him. Oh, don't believe him," cried Antony's mate in an agony of grief, unable to control herself, unable to believe that they could treat death so lightly. "He's not Antony, he is not my mate, he is Dick—Dick the Devil—the 'Jackal.' At least that's what they call him, but I know he is a lamb, led to the slaughter, willing to give his life for another."

There was a terrible to-do ! If this were true then the Little

Zoo army had made another mistake. Well, they couldn't help that, they must hang some animal, so it might as well be the ' Jackal ' as any other.

"Proceed with the hanging," shouted the Chief.

" That is, if it's all the same to you, Jackal," added Burgoyne, in his most exquisite manner.

And they proceeded.

They seized the ' Jackal,' bound him hand and foot, tied a rope round his neck, and . . .

At that terrible moment there was a great commotion ; and a raging, roaring Lion burst suddenly into their midst.

"Stop ! " he bellowed. " You've got hold of the wrong animal. I am the one you want. I am Antony, the Lamb," said he, roaring at the top of his voice !

" You a lamb ! " laughed Burgoyne, who always saw the funniness of everything ; " you look more like a lion to me ! "

" Ah—that's just it," said Antony. " One does not know oneself until the time comes. The ' Jackal ' here," said he, putting his arm affectionately round Dick, and taking the rope from his neck, " is the Lamb—a true disciple of the Lamb of God, whilst I, who thought I was—am a full-blooded Lion— at your service. I am now captain of the rebels with my army close on your heels."

Big Bug Burgoyne was clever enough to know when he was beaten. The rebels had got the upper hand. No wonder, with such a creature to lead them !

The Devil's Disciple

And they came to terms, the Little Zoo army was forced to clear out of their section and out of all the other sections.

And so the Little Zoo from over the Seas lost the great, big, tremendous United Zoo that Antony and Dick belonged to, because it made so many mistakes. But perhaps it is just as well, for the animals there have learned (or are learning) to manage themselves, and the Little Zoo over the Seas has enough to do in looking after herself and her other Zoos.

And Dick was free—free to be himself—and the Devil lost a disciple.

FANNY'S FIRST PLAY

or, What Can It Be?

FANNY'S FIRST PLAY
or, What Can It Be?

THERE was once a rare old bird who knew his own mind, so you can imagine what a rare old bird he was. But no ! I don't suppose you can, because you probably haven't enough sense to know what a rare thing it is to know your own mind, or to know a good thing when you see one. I may as well tell you that this story is going to be very rude : the sort of story that makes you as mad as anything. But perhaps it won't, though, because you'll never think you are one of the people I am referring to. You will, of course, think you are one of the few who do know their own mind and can recognize a rare good thing when you see it. So you will just go on in your own silly way thinking everyone else is one of the silly ones except yourself. You will, I know, because *I* do, and I know I am not sillier than you ; I can't possibly be, because I do know a rare old bird when I see one. Now you will think I am flattering myself. Oh, dear, I give it up—let's start all over again.

Once upon a time there was a rare old bird who knew his own mind, so you can imagine what a rare old bird he was—there, I've let you get away with it. Well, this rare old bird was bored—bored to death with everyone (or if he wasn't, he ought to have been) because nobody knew anything, couldn't see or hear or understand anything. Of course I don't mean they couldn't see or hear or understand anything when it was pointed out to them and had a proper label on it, telling them clearly what it was and what they ought to think about it. Of course they could see and understand then ; at least they could if the ones who put the labels on could. But could they ?

They were paid to know, I know ; but who paid them ? Only some of the silly ones who don't know their own minds and can't recognize a good thing when they see one. They can't because they haven't. They've had the old bird with them for ever so long and they haven't found the right label for him yet— they're always having to find new ones. In the beginning, when they first saw him, they were frightened out of their senses and labelled him

> SCORPION, DEADLY, DANGEROUS.

Then, when to their surprise they found that no one was actually poisoned to death by him, they changed their labels to

> MISCHIEVOUS, MOCKING, MOUNTEBANK.

Then, by degrees, they got so used to him that they did not take him seriously at all, and tore up the old tags and labelled him

> HUMORIST

and laughed at everything he said (no matter what he said).

And he laughs at them laughing—though if he wasn't such a rare old bird he might not be able to laugh—he might have to weep instead.

Of course he is a bit of a puzzle, I admit—I mean he is to all you who will have everything labelled and pigeon-holed. How on earth can you pigeon-hole a creature like the rare old bird ? How can he fit into any pigeon-hole ? He's like nothing on earth ! Just look at him—with his four feet and wings, neither a proper animal nor a proper bird ! Look at his appalling long tongue and the devilish twist to his tail, and his fiery eyes ! How can you label a thing like that ? You can't, you've just got to take him as he is. If you had any sense you would ; and you would sit and listen to him, with your own ears, and not rely on other people's. Fancy paying labellers to see and hear and understand for you ! It shows you're just as silly as they are, sillier in fact, because at least they get paid for their silliness.

Well, the rare old bird stood it all for a very long time, and then he made up his mind to play a joke on the labellers ; to show them up ; to prove to them that they don't know their own minds and can't recognize him when they see him. So he made an image of himself and sent it forth without putting his name on it, neither did he say what it was ; in fact, there was no clue on it whatsoever. Then he took himself off to watch the fun !

Four of the best labellers—the Sea Lion, the Carp, the Crab, and the Jelly Fish—caught sight of the strange thing and stared at it in consternation ; then they stared at each other. They didn't know what to think ; they couldn't make head or tail of it. They none of them wanted each other to know they didn't know, so they picked on the youngest—the Jelly Fish—and made him get out his box of labels first.

"Come on now, Jelly Fish, here's the creature before you—we call on you to label it first."

"You don't expect me to label a thing like that until I know who made it," retorted the Jelly Fish, quite surprised they should ask him.

"Why not ?" they all cried (scathingly !).

"Well, how do I know what sort of a creature it is ?" he demanded.

"Can't you tell by looking at it ?" said the others (still more scathingly !).

"Of course I can tell what it looks like, but how am I to know how to take it ? Is it a real creature, or is it a make-believe ? It looks queer enough to be anything."

"But is it a well-made creature, Jelly Fish ? That's all we're asking you to tell us—quite a simple question for you."

"Simple enough when you know who made it—that's the question I want answered first. You answer me that and I'll tell you soon enough whether it's well made or not. If it's made by a well-known creature, it's well made ; if it isn't, it isn't. That's simple enough for anyone. What do you think, Carp ?"

"It's easy enough to see who made it," said the Carp, gravely.

He made an image of himself

" You've only got to look at it carefully to know that. See those ears, taking in everything, and those silly wings—thinking it can rise to any heights ; when it's too jolly tame to even know how to use them properly, or be itself, or do anything but stick its tongue in its cheek, in imitation of the old bird ! Anybody with half an eye can see who made the thing."

" Who ? " they all cried breathlessly.

" Barker, the Dog, of course."

" *Bosh !* " said the Crab, contemptuously. " You've no perception at all—you can't see a thing when it's as plain as you are yourself. Why, it's obvious who made the horrid-looking thing, and if you care to listen to me, I will prove to you who made it."

" All right, we'll listen. Fire away, Crab."

" Well, first of all, it's a disagreeable creature, which proves that it can't have been made by Jam-Bareee—for all his images are dreamlike and pleasurable. Then it's got fire in its eye and feeling in its body, which jolly well proves that it isn't an image of the rare old bird, as everybody knows there's no fire or feeling in him. Now, look again, at that devil's tail, so cheap and tawdry, but still distinctive and showy, always appealing, always interesting, always human. Anyone with half an eye can guess who made it."

" Who ? " cried the others.

" Arthur Wing—the old Black Crow, of course."

The Jelly Fish wibbled and wobbled—he wasn't really as soft as he looked !

" I don't agree at all with what you say, Crab. You haven't said a word about the rare-old-bird touch that the Carp spotted —that inevitable tongue-in-the-cheek that's always trying to poke fun at everything, so as to get everyone talking about him—as we are now doing. I believe it's the rare old bird himself after all. What do you think, Sea Lion ? "

" Yes, Sea Lion, it's your turn," said the others. " What do you think ? "

At that moment there was a strange sound of laughing from above.

" Whatever's that ? " said the Jelly Fish, the Carp, and the Crab.

The Sea Lion had the sense to look up—he had a lot of that kind of sense—he had to have ; he had so much dignity to keep up ! He wasn't a lion for nothing ! He didn't know, of course —any more than the others—what to make of the strange image, or how to label it. He had been keeping very silent ; he couldn't afford to give himself away—not he. Well, as I said, he looked up—and there, to his amazement, was the rare old bird himself, chuckling with mischievous delight at all their wobbling, carping, and crabbing.

Now the rare old bird was a friend of the Sea Lion, and took pity on him and determined to preserve his dignity for him by saving him from having to label his image without knowing who made it. So he made signs to him, telling him it was an image of himself.

The Sea Lion was tremendously relieved by his miraculous escape, and, regaining his composure and grandeur, prepared himself to deliver his verdict.

"I should say, decidedly, that this unique creature is a faithful impression of the rare old bird. The length of his tongue, the twist in his tail, the audacity of his having two pairs of feet, together with a pair of wings, in his endeavour to confuse us and destroy all existing conventions, his invulnerable body, making him impervious to the opinions of his fellows, with, of course, the inevitable twinkle in his eye by which he is clever enough to disarm everybody, leaves no doubt whatever in my mind that the creature is the image of the rare old bird."

Then going to his box of stale, old, humorous labels he picked out this one—

| DRAGON: |
| DARING, AMUSING, IMAGERY |

and laid it with a magnificent gesture upon the waters !

But the tide has long since washed it away ! The image remains, and will remain, for all of us to label to our heart's content.

And some day some one might find a real good label—that will stick !